SPACECRAFT EARTH

A GUIDE FOR PASSENGERS

Dr Henry Richter
with David F. Coppedge

Spacecraft Earth: A Guide for Passengers
by Dr Henry Richter with David F. Coppedge

First printing: September 2017

ISBN 978-1-942773-48-1

Cover illustration: J. Beverly Greene
Design and layout: Keaton Halley

Published by

Creation Book Publishers
P.O. Box 350
Powder Springs, GA 30127
Phone: 1-800-616-1264
creationbookpublishers.com

Please visit our website for further information on the Christian worldview and the creation/evolution issue:

CREATION.com

ACKNOWLEDGEMENTS

M y first acknowledgment is to my wife of 47 years, dear Beverly. Her encouragement and journey with me has been my driving force. Also, as my in-house editor, she usually adds a thousand or so commas to my writings. Thanks also to David Coppedge who agreed to sharpen this writing and to augment many of the illustrations of phenomena and earth features. To Dr John Hartnett for his refinements of chapter 6. To Dr Mark Harwood of *Creation Ministries International* (CMI) who did the final editorial reshaping of the text which added the professional touch to *Spacecraft Earth*. Finally to Keaton Halley, also of CMI, who did a phenomenal job of finding illustrations, and formatting and architecting the text.

TABLE OF CONTENTS

Foreword

I was only seven years old when Dr Henry Richter's instruments inside the Explorer I satellite were lofted into orbit atop Wernher von Braun's Jupiter-C rocket on January 31, 1958. But even as a kid, I knew something big had happened! The contest between Sputnik and Explorer launched my own interest in space that has lasted a lifetime. After leading dozens of star parties and writing hundreds of popular articles on astronomy, little did I know that I would meet a rocket pioneer almost 50 years later and become his friend, and eventually an assistant for his book.

Having received separate bachelor's degrees in science education and astrophysics, I, too, had a chance to work at NASA's prestigious Jet Propulsion Laboratory (JPL) where Dr Richter had helped make history so long before. For 14 years, from 1996 to 2011, with a talented team of over 300 scientists and engineers, I played a 'bit part' in the drama of Cassini—JPL's most ambitious outer planet mission ever, the tour of Saturn. It was a fantastic experience to be at the lab, witnessing firsthand Cassini's many major discoveries, including the first soft landing on Titan by the Huygens Probe. I was there for the launch, cruise and tour, all the way into its second extended mission. For 9 of those years, I was Team Lead of the ground systems computer administration group, responsible for most of the computers on the program.

In 2007, a gentleman in his senior years called, asking if he could meet me for lunch at the lab. He had read some of my science articles and was interested in getting acquainted. I nearly fell off my chair during that lunch when I realized who I was talking to: one of the great pioneers of space exploration, who had helped manage that

Explorer I mission I had followed on radio and TV as a kid. And he was calling on me? I was stunned, but I found Henry to be a gracious, humble man who shared similar views about life and the universe. We quickly became friends (and I must add that his wife Beverly is equally gracious and kind). Whenever he stopped by the lab to do research for a book he was writing on Explorer I,[1] Henry would look me up and we would chat over lunch.

I remember the big 50th Anniversary celebration for Explorer I at JPL, on January 31st, 2008. Dr Richter, one of the only surviving managers of the Explorer I team, was the most honored VIP that day among many space veterans who came, some from long distances. I have a DVD of his talk at the lab, wherein he shared some of his views you will read about in this book. That year, he also received high honors in Washington DC at a black-tie awards ceremony along with the surviving JPL Directors. Later, in 2014, he was a guest of honor at the 50th anniversary of the Deep Space Network he had helped establish.

This book represents Dr Henry Richter's first-person account of views he developed about the big questions of the universe. As he takes you logically through the observations that led to his conclusions, I'm content to just hide in the background, steering a bit of wording or sentence structure here or there, so that his message can be effectively communicated to as wide an audience as possible. I know you will enjoy thinking along with the clear-minded reasoning of this Caltech instructor and JPL rocket scientist: a great American, and a gentleman.

David Coppedge
Associate Producer, Illustra Media

ENDNOTES

1. Richter, Henry L., *America's Leap Into Space: My Time at JPL and the First Explorer Satellites*, Friesen Press, 2015.

Introduction

Ah, the Earth — a really remarkable place, and which we call HOME. I would like you to explore the earth with me to see what a phenomenal object it is. I am sure it is unique in the universe, although there are an uncountable number of stars, many of which have planets. But just being a planet does not include the possibility of being able to support life, much less complex, intelligent life. In this book we will learn about all the myriad of features that allow life to exist: being attached to a stable star, for instance, and having an orbital radius that allows a narrow range of favorable temperatures. Our planet's rotation of 24 hours is just right; imagine a 1-hour day, or a 90-hour day! Having water in abundance, and a suitable atmosphere are crucial, too; they allow metabolism and provide protection from the radiation of space. Having the right mix of minerals available, which the earth does, is vital. I will go into much of this later.

This book is the result of a number of friends urging me to put into writing some of the content of talks that I have given about my life and scientific interest. By way of introduction, I am a PhD from Caltech (California Institute of Technology in Pasadena, CA) and a former 'rocket scientist.' I was honored as a 'Spaceflight Pioneer' in 2008, during the 50th anniversary of the first U.S. Earth Satellite Explorer I. The American Institute of Aeronautics and Astronautics awarded the Jet Propulsion Laboratory the Annual Achievement Award, and I was invited to receive the Award along with the present JPL Director and the three surviving former JPL Directors. It was quite a time with about 2500 in attendance at the banquet in Washington D.C., with everyone in 'black tie.'

As further background, I have always been interested in science and in finding out the cause behind a variety of things. I started by experimenting with a chemistry set when in the third grade. My parents were art teachers in the local high school, and so the next summer when they needed some place to park me, the high school chemistry teacher allowed me to sit in on the chemistry summer school course. I excelled in the

Award ceremony
Dr Richter (2ⁿᵈ from left), along with the JPL team, receiving the AIAA Annual Achievement Award, 2008.

sciences in high school. We lived in the semi-rural community of Rolling Hills in southern Los Angeles County. My parents built a laboratory building onto the garage for me in high school days.

This was during World War II, and I cut my high school time by one semester to enter the U.S. Navy. Because I had a ham radio license, I was able to sign up to become an electronic technician and went through the Navy schools. The war ended about this time, and my short 16 month's career in the Navy came to a close. I managed to gain acceptance into a fine school, the California Institute of Technology, or Caltech as it was called. After leaving the Navy and before starting Caltech, I went to Northwestern University in Evanston, Illinois for one semester and then got married. I was just marking time at Northwestern waiting to get into Caltech and only took three courses: geology, the philosophy of ethics and morals, and English.

When I started attending Caltech, I did well, and because of my first-term grades, I was placed in the 'honor section.' Because of my primary interest in chemistry, I elected chemistry as a major. I took a pretty typical physical science course schedule, and for an elective, I took genetics instead of astronomy. I undertook several undergraduate research projects, one of which was in the physics department, and another in the analytical chemistry department. These all fed into my curiosity about the universe and what made it tick. I also took on several summer jobs which fed into my staple of skills and knowledge. I might also mention that by the time I came to the end of my undergraduate years, my wife and I had three children. This is known as an additional incentive to get a career going and develop some income.

I also did graduate work at Caltech, graduating with a PhD with a major in Chemistry and minors in Physics and Electrical Engineering. I went to work at the Jet Propulsion Laboratory (JPL) in the mid-1950's when the space program was just starting. JPL was operated by Caltech, and was a great place to go to work. At the time, it was a guided-missile research and development organization, part of the U.S. Army. It was associated with the Redstone Arsenal in Huntsville, Alabama, where Dr Wernher von Braun was Director. Although not part of our recognized mission, we developed an earth satellite and a launch vehicle, hoping someday to put a satellite into orbit. Our chance came when in 1957 the Russians launched their Sputniks, and the U.S. government gave us the go-ahead to launch our little 30-pound satellite. It was successful. It carried a Cosmic Ray experiment for Dr James A. Van Allen which discovered the radiation belts around the earth, named the Van Allen belts in his honor. NASA (the National Aeronautics and Space Administration) was formed shortly afterwards, and JPL became part of NASA with the role of exploring the moon, the planets, and deep space.

So I came to learn quite a bit about this earth on which we reside, the solar system, and the universe in general. Along the way, I realized that we live on a very unique body that could be likened to a spacecraft: Spacecraft Earth. I also began to realize that many of the characteristics of earth appeared to be uniquely appropriate to the existence of life, and even to the human species. I want to develop that line of observation and reasoning in this book. Almost any physical characteristic of the earth, its structure and composition, and position in the solar system is the way it is to permit the existence of life. From the properties of atoms, the elements, compounds, to the exact composition and placement of the earth, everything seems to be the way it is to allow life to flourish here.

Many unrelated phenomena come together in a special way to allow life to exist. These include the hydrogen bonds that make water unique among most substances, the habitable zone around the sun, and the existence of a moon the right mass and distance from our planet, with its beneficial effects on the oceans. In later chapters of this book, we will glimpse into this amazing catalog of seemingly unconnected physical facts, each of which is important to the existence of life on our unique spacecraft.

But let me introduce the most sophisticated example of physical organization on this earth—the one most important to us passengers on our spaceship—and that is the human body. There is a widely taught and believed school of thought that we came about through a process called evolution, the result of random, undirected events in nature over an extremely long period of time.

I must admit that for a long time I was in the evolution camp due to my education. In geology class at Northwestern, we studied the widely-accepted history of the world and the universe. We took field trips collecting fossils of little marine animals called trilobites in the shale rocks south of Chicago. I was well schooled in the consensus view of the progression of species from the first life ending with our species, *Homo sapiens*. I was told that we not only evolved ourselves, but we inhabit an evolving universe that started billions of years ago with a horrific explosion from an extremely hot, dense state of energy that produced *everything*. Where this energy came from, or what was there before, no one knew.

For a long time I did not question this explanation, but as I learned more about the universe, the earth, and life, I began to have doubts about what I had been taught and what was generally believed. After leaving the space program in early NASA days, I developed a real amazement at the nature and complexity of the world around me, and particularly of intelligent human life.

So let's begin by checking out our spacecraft and its features. Following that, we'll examine our own equipment: the human body. We'll encounter some amazing animals and plants next—some of our fellow passengers—and ask where they and the first living cells came from. After that, we'll get into the subject of the 'big bang' (which you are free to skip, if you get bogged down in the mathematics or heavy concepts in that chapter). We'll try thinking outside the box with some parts of earth hard to explain according to traditional ideas. Finally, to tie this all together, I'll share the story of my personal journey into big questions about what it all means. Hopefully by the conclusion we will all gain a deeper understanding of our own personal journeys on this amazing Spacecraft Earth.

Dr Henry Richter
Former Space Instruments Section Manager, NASA/JPL

1

The Spacecraft: Planet Earth

Our understanding of the universe has grown steadily since the invention of the telescope 400 years ago. But less than 100 years ago, we did not even know for sure if the Milky Way was the only galaxy. Now, we know about hundreds of billions of galaxies! From a distant vantage point, the large scale structure of the universe would look like a vast web, composed of clusters and superclusters of galaxies, with huge voids between them. One of the clusters is a special one to us, called the Local Cluster. Within that cluster, one galaxy stands out in our minds: the Milky Way. Within a spiral arm of that galaxy, a very special star carries a family of planets around it: our solar system. And within that solar system is one planet with all the right conditions for life. That planet is our Spacecraft Earth, giving its abundant variety of life-forms a first-class ride through the universe.

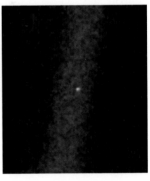

NASA/JPL

Figure 1-1. Pale blue dot
Planet Earth (bright speck in the center) as seen from the edge of the solar system. Photo taken by Voyager 1.

In the big scheme of things, the earth might appear insignificant. It's such a tiny speck, that even from the orbit of Pluto it would attract little notice. Be that as it may, there are more ways to measure significance than mere size. Our solar system has some very remarkable features: among them, a safe location in the Milky Way, a stable star, and a habitable zone far from giant planets. These features, and others we will consider briefly, are—as far as we know—actually quite rare. For instance, other planetary systems we've discovered around other stars look nothing like our solar system. Their giant planets often are found orbiting very close to their host stars, even closer than Mercury is to our sun. Earth could not coexist with one of those 'hot Jupiters' were our sun's family to follow that pattern. Fortunately, the sun's habitable zone is occupied with one (and only one) planet in a stable orbit with the perfect combination of features to permit complex life.

As audacious as it might sound, I would venture to say that the earth is a unique body in the whole universe. It contains all of the chemical and physical features that are necessary to allow life to exist. To date, there is only one place we know of in the entire universe that has life—and we are riding on that spaceship right now. The improbability of finding another planet as life-friendly as the earth becomes evident when we start considering the many requirements for life. Whatever feature of the earth one is willing to consider in detail appears to be uniquely tailored to promote the existence of not just any life, but large, complex organisms like human beings. In this chapter, we will consider just a few.

Now, I realize that there are all sorts of conjectures about life on other planets and on planets around other stars, but I would submit that even if life were discovered on Mars, Europa or Titan—some of the leading candidates for life-permitting habitats beyond earth—those objects could in no way provide the kind of support systems where life could flourish. At best, only microbes might exist, buried deep under the Martian soil, swimming several miles down under the icy crust of Europa, or frozen in perpetual darkness in a Titan lake. How different from Spacecraft Earth! Indeed, there are very few places on earth where life is *not* thriving in abundance. What accounts for the difference?

Construction

Let's start with the chemical and physical composition of the earth. Life as we know it could not exist in significant numbers if the chemical and physical parameters that characterize the earth were changed even by a small amount. For instance, complex life needs oxygen enough to breathe, but not so much that wildfires would become more prevalent and catastrophic. The right balance is maintained by marine organisms in a sophisticated feedback loop. Responding to the amount of phosphorus eroded from the continents, oceanic microbes bloom and produce more oxygen if levels drop. When there is too much oxygen, other organisms deposit the excess phosphorus in the deep sea sediments.[1]

Examination of the chemistry and composition of the earth shows numerous factors conducive to life—whether it be an abundance of water, a gaseous oxidizing atmosphere, or the availability of necessary chemical elements. We'll hear about bromine in the next chapter, an element only recently found to be essential. That's just one of 28 elements out of the 92 naturally occurring elements that must be present near the surface of the earth in sufficient quantities for multicellular life to flourish. Even some so-called 'trace elements' have been shown to be important for animals and plants.

Here's a particularly notable instance at the atomic scale. As most people learn in chemistry, most substances, when they change from the liquid state to the solid state (that is, when they freeze), become more dense. As a result, whether the substance is iron or candle wax, when the liquid and solid forms are added together, the solid sinks to the bottom. There is a rare exception to this rule: water. It also happens to be the most abundant molecule on the surface of the 'water planet,' the earth.

Figure 1-2. Mouse ears
Molecular diagram of water—one part oxygen, two parts hydrogen

The water molecule is a remarkable device. It consists of one oxygen atom and two hydrogen atoms, the familiar 'H_2O.' Electrical forces between the atoms bring the two hydrogens closer together, where they stabilize at an angle of 104.5°, giving the water molecule a 'mouse ears' shape. This conformation is critical to water's unique properties. It explains the highly unusual fact that when water freezes into ice, it expands. As crystals of ice form, the 'mouse ear' molecules arrange into more open structures, or lattices, than they normally would. Because of this expansion, ice is less dense than water, and it floats! This property is vital for life on earth.

Consider what would happen if ice did not float. In winter, water would freeze and sink to the bottom of lakes, rivers, and the ocean, accumulating into increasingly thick layers of ice. The warming summer air would not penetrate those deep layers. Only some of the ice at the surface would be able to melt, resulting in shallow ponds of water on top of deep, perpetual layers of ice. Over the course of time, almost all of the water on earth would freeze. True, there could be a couple of centimeters of liquid water on top of the ice on a hot day, but without abundant liquid water on the earth in oceans and lakes, life would have a most difficult time surviving. There would certainly be no significant life existing in shallow bodies of water if the bottoms were frozen. But because ice floats, much of the water underneath can stay liquid, allowing fish to survive under the ice of many lakes (that's why ice fishing is popular in many high latitudes). Without this unique property of the water molecule, Spacecraft Earth would likely turn into a giant snowball. This is due not only to the shape of the water molecule, but its specific heat—its ability to store much more heat than most other liquids.

Water gives up a great deal of heat when it freezes. It therefore takes considerable heat to melt ice in bodies of water. The heat required to melt ice at zero degrees Celsius (0°C) is 80 calories per gram. This means that to melt one gram of ice would take one gram of water at 80°C, and the result would be two grams of water now at 0°C. So, water of just a few degrees above the temperature of ice melts very little.

Why does water behave this way, becoming less dense when it freezes? The answer lies in the 'hydrogen bond'—a chemical property that received considerable attention from Dr Linus Pauling, recipient of two unshared Nobel Prizes, and one of my mentors at Caltech. Dr Pauling noticed a strange, unexplainable attraction between the hydrogen atoms in adjacent water molecules that causes them to line up in remarkable ways when water freezes. Because of this, the molecular structure stretches out slightly, thus producing lower density in the ice. So simple a molecule, but so profound! To this day, chemists have not explained all the remarkable properties of water and ice. Time would fail us to explore its many other unique life-enabling properties. From the glory of a snowflake to the global water cycle, this clear, beautiful substance graces our photographs, brings laughter to children at the pool, and courses through every cell in our bodies. Life would be inconceivable without water. That's why most astrobiologists consider liquid water to be a requirement for any habitable zone anywhere in the universe.

Another unique chemical element is carbon. Because of special characteristics of the carbon atom, it can form all sorts of combinations with itself and other atoms to form what are called 'organic compounds.' There are literally millions of different chemical combinations possible. The very name 'organic' comes from the fact that carbon is the basic building block of all living organisms, although many organic molecules are not involved in life.

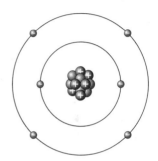

Figure 1-3. Carbon atom
The unique chemistry of carbon makes it ideal for use in living things.

Compounds of carbon include acids, esters, alcohols, and many, many other kinds. In our bodies, the carbohydrates, fats and sugars we consume are all carbon compounds. Carbon is found in the amino acids that combine into proteins and enzymes that make up our skin, blood, organs, arteries and veins, and everything else that gives our body structure and function. Carbon is found in the nucleotides that combine into DNA that stores our genetic information. Most astrobiologists would concur: no carbon, no life. No other element has the ideal properties of carbon. Some science fiction writers have tried to imagine life based on silicon. In the real world, though, silicon tends to form rocks, not the pliable, flexible forms we see in carbon-based life. Life needs carbon. Fortunately, this also is found in abundance on Spacecraft Earth.

Environmental tolerances

Let us consider the physics of the earth. One of the first considerations is temperature. Earth experiences a narrow range of temperatures that is rare in space. We think we know what unbearably hot or cold days feel like, but the universe experiences highs in the millions of degrees in the interiors of stars, down to near absolute zero on some lonely, dark, isolated planets. Temperatures at the surface of earth range from -128.6°F (-89.2°C) at Antarctica to 134°F (57°C) in Death Valley, but those are uncommon. Most of the biosphere never experiences those extremes. Some microbes are even adapted to living in the near-boiling waters of hot springs. Whole ecosystems have been found at scalding hydrothermal vents at the bottom of the sea, where nearby fish swim in cold, perpetual darkness. But those are exceptions; most plants and animals live within a narrower band of the already-narrow set of temperatures on earth. Within earth's more common temperature ranges, we see plants and reptiles thriving in deserts, plants pushing their new leaves up through the snow, and gibbons swinging from branch to branch in tropical jungles. What an amazing world is our home!

There has been much concern of late regarding the fate of the biosphere if average global temperatures were to rise. Concern about the existence and effects of what are called 'greenhouse gases' have received international attention. Alarmed scientists worry that just a few degrees rise in average global temperatures could have drastic consequences on life by melting polar icecaps, raising sea levels, inundating coastal areas, and rendering farmland unproductive with severe droughts. In the past, other climatologists have worried about the prospect of another ice age. The fossil record shows past excursions of higher and lower temperatures on parts of the earth. The fact that life has endured past climate swings suggests that the earth has 'feedback' mechanisms to keep its temperatures from deadly extremes. Some climate models show, for instance, that an increase in temperature would increase cloud cover, which would have the effect of reflecting more of the sun's energy back out to space. As important as these concerns are, we should not fail to recognize that they imply that earth's climate is finely tuned to support the biosphere.

Earth's temperature is determined, to first order, by our type of star and our distance from it. You can 'count your lucky star' by considering our sun's remarkable properties. Fortunately for us, it is one of the most stable, predictable stars known. Occasionally we hear worries about flares and 'coronal mass ejections' that threaten our electrical grid and satellite communications, but the sun's bad days are mild compared to the angry outbursts from the majority of stars. 'Superflares' from red dwarf stars, the most numerous type, would quickly fry any life on a planet in its habitable zone. Many giant stars, at the other end of the size scale, emit so much ionizing radiation, they would render their planets sterile.

Our sun emits a 'solar constant' (energy received at earth's surface) of 1.361 kilowatts per square meter. At solar maximum (the period in the sun's 11-year cycle when its activity increases to its highest level), the heat received at the earth increases by just one tenth of one percent—an extremely slight difference. One of the longest running scientific observations ever made of the sun measured only 0.06% variation from the solar constant over a 32-year period.[2] That makes our sun one of the quietest among quiet stars. Without a predictable energy supply, life would only survive under great duress—not just because of the variations themselves, but because of the aftereffects they would initiate, some perhaps irreversible. If the atmosphere were ever stripped away during a severe solar outburst, for instance, it might never come back. If earth froze solid during a cold period, on the other hand, it might remain frozen thereafter. It takes the right kind of star—a very predictable, reliable one—to support life.

The properties of earth, too, determine its temperature. When we tune in to weather forecasters giving us the predicted highs and lows for the day, we don't usually have to worry about dying from heat or cold, provided we dress appropriately. Even on the most extreme weather days, the highs and lows are very mild compared to what they could be. We can tell by looking at the moon next door. Without an atmosphere and crust like ours, lunar temperatures rise and fall rapidly and severely. Under direct sunlight, the moon heats up to 253°F (123°C), but then drops down to -243°F (-153°C) at lunar night. The Apollo astronauts had to land, do their work, and leave during narrow orbital windows when it was safe. Even so, their spacesuits had to carefully control body temperature, as well as supply oxygen. They could not have survived for a minute without bringing a bit of earth's habitat with them to surround themselves. Even a small leak could have proved fatal. Some of the astronauts remarked about how intense the glare of the sun was without an atmosphere. Had charged particles from a large solar flare come at them while they were on the surface, they would have died in minutes—because the moon has no protective magnetic field. That's another factor that protects life on earth. We will not take the time here to discuss it in detail, except to say that space travel is like wandering through a cosmic 'shooting gallery' when you move outside the earth's protective magnetic field. This is of grave concern to planners of future Mars missions, when astronauts would be exposed to the solar wind and cosmic rays for three years at a time or more. Of the inner planets, only the earth has a magnetic field large enough to protect its inhabitants. (We will consider the magnetic field in more detail in Chapter 7.)

Why the difference in temperature extremes between two bodies, the earth and the moon, at the same distance from the sun? The answers are in the properties of our atmosphere, oceans, and crust. Each plays a part in absorbing, reflecting, and radiating heat according to well-known laws of thermodynamics. The atmosphere filters the sunlight, keeping out the deadliest ultraviolet rays but letting in the 'rainbow spectrum' of colors most useful to plants and animals, with energies just right for photosynthesis and for chemical reactions in cells. The oceans absorb vast quantities of heat and release it slowly, setting up atmospheric and oceanic currents in a glorious dance that circulates the energy to all parts of the globe. The continents, mostly silicates and carbonates, possess enough 'thermal inertia' to store and release energy slowly. These factors moderate earth's temperature to avoid extremes.

Habitability

A 'habitable zone' is the orbital radius around a star where liquid water—and presumably life—could exist. As we shall see, there's a lot more required for life than just being 'in the zone'. Earth's distance from the sun—ranging from 91.4 million to 94.5 million miles (average about 92.9 million miles or 150 million kilometers)—keeps it always within the habitable zone. That zone is pretty narrow. Venus is well outside the inner edge and Mars is outside the outer edge. If the Earth's average distance from the sun were 5 percent greater (some astronomers estimate just 1% greater), temperatures would drop such that most of the Earth's water would freeze in a 'runaway ice age.' If the Earth were just 1 to 5 percent closer to the sun, on the other hand, the polar caps would melt, more water would evaporate, and a 'runaway greenhouse effect' would ensue, turning Earth into an inhospitable hothouse.

But that's just one of the numbers in the 'cosmic lottery' that Spacecraft Earth got right. More thinking about habitable zones has added further requirements. From the literature of astrobiology, we can identify ten or more other 'zones' required for habitability, in addition to circumstellar distance:

- **Galactic Habitable Zone:** the solar system must occupy a narrow band within the galaxy.

- **Continuously Habitable Zone:** the habitable zone must not vary significantly.

- **Temporal Habitable Zone:** the habitable zone must last long enough for life to persist.

- **Chemical and Thermodynamic Habitable Zone:** the planet's chemistry and heat transfer mechanisms must permit liquid water to persist.

- **Ultraviolet Habitable Zone:** the planet must filter out ionizing radiation from its star.

- **Tidal Habitable Zone:** the star must not tidally 'lock' its habitable planet to force one hemisphere to always face the star (this rules out most planets).

- **Obliquity Habitable Zone:** the star must not 'erase' its habitable planet's tilt through tidal forces. (While not eliminating the possibility of life, a planet without a tilt would have no seasons, drastically reducing its habitable surface area.)

- **Eccentricity Habitable Zone:** the planet must have a nearly circular orbit so that it stays in the zone.

- **Stellar Chemistry Habitable Zone:** the star must have the right chemical composition to remain quiet and well-behaved. A G2 main-sequence star like our sun is ideal.

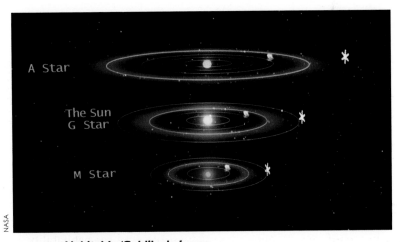

Figure 1-4. **Habitable 'Goldilocks' zone**
The narrow orbital radius around a star in which life can exist, seen in different star types

- **Stellar Wind Habitable Zone:** the star must not be given to extreme 'space weather' that might strip off a habitable planet's atmosphere.

- **Inhabited Zone:** recently, two astrobiologists suggested that to be habitable, a planet needs inhabitants! "…there is a growing amount of evidence supporting the idea that our Planet will not be the same if we remove every single form of life from its surface," a news report said.[3]

In thinking over all the factors, a planetary scientist at the University of Arizona said, "Habitability is very difficult to quantify because it depends on a huge number of variables, some of which we have yet to identify."[4] It's likely, therefore, that this is only a partial list. Spacecraft Earth scores an 'A' on them all.

Our satellite

One particularly intriguing thing about Spacecraft Earth is its moon. It's not only beautiful; it may be required for life to flourish. Approximately a quarter million miles away, with an orbital period of approximately 28 days (a 'moon-th' or month), our moon has just the properties to benefit life in several ways. As moons go, ours is extraordinarily large in relation to its planet's diameter. This is another unique feature of Spacecraft Earth that is quite remarkable. Our moon is an enormous object with significant gravity, roughly one-sixth of that of the earth, as you may recall from watching videos of Apollo astronauts cheerfully leaping high from the surface. No other planet in the solar system (with the exception of Pluto, a 'dwarf planet') has a moon so large relative to its size. Mercury and Venus have no moon; Mars has two tiny satellites. The gas giants have some moons larger than ours, but they are very small relative to the planets themselves.

The moon stabilizes the earth's axis, preventing wild swings in obliquity that would wreak havoc with the seasons. Another very noticeable benefit of having a large moon is regulation of the tides. The moon is much smaller than the sun, but because it is much closer, its gravity has a more pronounced effect, causing both land and sea to rise and fall in a daily rhythm. Because rock is more resistant to tidal pull than water, the oceans are affected the most. As the earth rotates, and the moon revolves around it, gravity sets up powerful ocean currents we only partially notice at high tide and low tide. These currents are amplified when the moon and sun are in line with the earth. Because the bodies are constantly moving, there is a time delay in their effects on the earth, so that high tides are some hours after the alignment. A variety of marine organisms, from fish to turtles to worms, regulate their spawning very precisely by the lunar tides.

The orbital choreography between sun, moon and earth also pumps energy into the oceans independent of solar heating, creating a huge engine that provides several benefits for life. It cleanses the coastlines, it circulates nutrients between latitudes, and it forces some of the deep water to the surface and back again. All this energy input contributes to the weather, too, by increasing evaporation and cloud formation.

Although the tides are not anything spectacular toward the equator, or even along the coasts of North America, we find that in the higher latitudes such as Anchorage the diurnal tidal action can amount to 20, 30 or 40 feet of rise and fall. That's a lot of water to lift. The results of this pumping action are profound interactions between sea and land, sea and atmosphere, and between shallow and deep ocean waters, down to hundreds and even thousands of feet. Simultaneously, other nutrients are washed into the ocean by rivers, carrying their sediment loads to the sea, thanks to clouds generated in part by the lunar engine. In this way, the moon links the atmosphere and the land with the deep ocean.

Oxygenated by the tides, the ocean waters are then transported and mixed at various depths around the globe by strong currents, where numerous creatures await the bounty. Fish can extract this oxygen by passing seawater through their gills, similar to the way land animals extract oxygen with their lungs. The moon therefore plays a very significant role in the vitality of the marine ecosystem. Ocean life, without direct access to the oxygen in the atmosphere, is able to obtain vital elements for extracting energy from food— thanks to the tidal engine provided by our moon.

It would be a very stale world without a moon like ours. Most likely, the biosphere would be severely impoverished. The opposite extreme—too large a moon, or too close—would be devastating as well, with tides that might run clear across continents, driving extreme weather that could destroy life. Here we see another

'Goldilocks' factor that came together just right at Spacecraft Earth. But there's more: some things about the moon seem particularly beneficial for humans.

A privileged platform

The moon is a romantic subject, for sure; a lovely sight to share with a friend. It also provides helpful light at 'Harvest Moon' for farmers working late to bring in the crops. But one of the most interesting facts about the moon for human consideration is a particular coincidence that has intrigued many an astronomer: its ability to create total eclipses. The moon's diameter is 400 times smaller than the sun, but the moon is 400 times closer. At certain times in its elliptical orbit, the moon comes in front of the sun, and is just the right size to cover it completely. Sometimes the match is perfect. Anyone who has witnessed a total solar eclipse knows how thrilling the experience is! The sky goes dark, the stars appear, and the gleaming corona of the sun, like a dazzling silver crown, explodes into view around the black circle of the moon's disk.

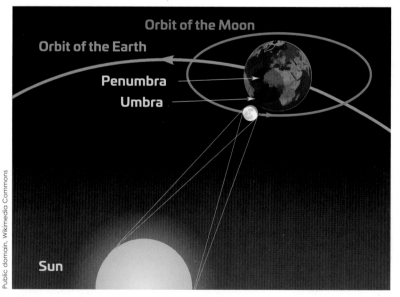

Figure 1-5. **Geometry of a total solar eclipse**
The moon and the sun have the same apparent size to an observer on earth, making total solar eclipses a wonder to behold.

Emotionally engaging as total eclipses can be, their intellectual significance is even greater. Because the 'clockwork of the heavens' makes eclipses predictable to the second, historians have been able to date important ancient events by records of eclipses left by contemporary observers. Additionally, solar eclipses have allowed astronomers to view parts of the sun's atmosphere that cannot be seen at any other time, particularly the chromosphere and corona. Over a hundred years ago, a spectrum of the chromosphere taken during a total eclipse led to the discovery of helium. Other major astrophysical discoveries quickly followed, shedding light on the nature of stars and galaxies. In 1919, Sir Arthur Eddington

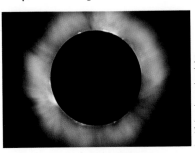

Figure 1-6. Total solar eclipse
The perfect match between the apparent sizes of the sun and moon allowed the sun's atmosphere to be investigated, which led to the discovery of the element helium.

Luc Viatour / www.Lucnix.be

confirmed a prediction of Albert Einstein by measuring relativistic shifts in starlight during a total eclipse. Relativity theory, dramatically confirmed in this way, has had an enormous impact on human understanding of the entire universe.

This story is told by astrobiologist Guillermo Gonzalez and philosopher Jay Richards in their book, *The Privileged Planet*.[5] They also appear in a documentary film by that name.[6] Gonzalez and Richards point to a number of peculiar coincidences about earth and the universe, including total eclipses, which have made possible many important scientific discoveries. Gonzalez calculated that within our solar system, only the earth has total solar eclipses. What a 'coincidence' that only Spacecraft Earth is also the only body with intelligent observers who can appreciate them and use them.

It is clear that the effect of the moon on life is profound. If the moon were farther away, or less massive, the lunar 'engine' would be weaker, leaving all life impoverished of its beneficial mixing effects. On the other hand, if the moon were closer to the earth, with the same mass, the tidal action would become strong enough to erode the continents down to sea level, leaving a 'water world' subject to horrendous currents. Instead, the moon is 'just right'—another cosmological accident?

These are just a few considerations on an astronomical scale. At the other extreme—the atomic scale—we find the same pattern of factors seeming to 'conspire' to support life on Spacecraft Earth. The peculiar behaviors of certain chemical substances (particularly water), as we have seen, play crucial roles for earth's habitability. This supports a principle stated earlier: if one examines carefully almost any phenomenon of the earth or the physical laws that govern it, it will turn out to be critical for the existence of life.

Are there other travelers out there?

There is eager interest among some in the scientific community and the general public to detect life beyond earth. Whether it is trying to find signs of life on Mars or on some distant exoplanet, NASA and other space agencies are actively searching for life in programs called Astrobiology and SETI (the Search for Extra-Terrestrial Intelligence). There seems to be a desperate determination to prove that we are not unique in the universe.

In support of the search, they like to point out how many stars there are. The universe is indeed huge. There are probably more stars than there are grains of sand on the earth. Just think about all that sand—how uncountable it seems. You would think that from just a probability argument, there are enough suns that there are bound to be many planets that could support life—not just life, but intelligent life. However, as we pointed out for habitable zones, many other factors need to be considered when assessing the probability. Here are a few more.

The sun must have an energy output and size as to give the right amount of heat to a planet in the habitable zone, and that means a main sequence G2 dwarf star. Only about 1% of all stars fall into this class, and many are not as quiet as our sun. The associated star, furthermore, must be stable in its energy output. Any significant temporal variation of the heat output would cause catastrophic swings in the temperature of the planet which would be destructive of life forms.

The orbit in which a candidate planet travels must be nearly circular within the habitable zone, again for temperature regulation. Life depends on what might be called 'reasonable' chemical reactions, and these are very temperature-dependent. The temperature at which most life related reactions occur is above the freezing point of water and well below the boiling point, so the location in the habitable zone must be such as to result in moderate temperatures.

To survive destructive impacts of space objects and debris, it would best be protected by gas giant planets in its planetary system.

The rate of rotation is important to have a reasonable length of night and day. A rotation rate of one hour would be too short for life cycles to get rest and activity. A rotation rate of once a month would be too long for night-to-day changes. A rotation rate of 24 hours seems just about right—how about that?

The mass of the planet needs to be in the proper range to produce gravity large enough to keep an atmosphere, but not too much atmosphere which would have high pressures.

Water must not just be abundant, but available. It cannot be all buried under the crust, for example. The water must be pure enough to allow life; only then can it provide a source of food. The water must be of a temperature favorable to the existence and growth of living cells. Most of the planet's water must also have neutral pH, the balance between acidity and alkalinity.

Along with water, an atmosphere is necessary. Our atmosphere gives us oxygen for utilizing the nutrients in our cells. The ratio of molecules in the atmosphere is also crucial. An atmosphere of pure oxygen would be too rich for cells, making them self-destruct, leading to catastrophic wildfires on the land as well. The mixture of roughly 20% reactive oxygen and 80% neutral nitrogen seems ideal for life as we know it. The atmosphere also protects us from harmful

NASA/Reid Wiseman

Figure 1-7. **Remarkable atmosphere**
Earth has enough atmosphere to sustain life, but not so much as to produce crushing pressure.

radiation from the sun. The sun gives off damaging ultraviolet light, most of which is filtered out by the upper atmosphere. Our atmosphere shields us from the high-energy subatomic particles that could disrupt cells. So of all the atmospheres possible on other worlds, the composition and ratios of elements are critical. We are starting to develop a stringent set of criteria that must accompany any exoplanet under consideration for life.

Another key feature that is needed to protect the surface of a planet from destructive effects of a star is a magnetic field. Our magnetic field deflects the streams of solar electrons and protons, so that most of them do not penetrate the atmosphere. It's clear that any planet must have a magnetic field to support complex life, and, moreover, a field that is not too strong and not too weak. If too strong, it might disrupt the planet's crust. If too weak, it could not deflect charged particles. This important factor will be considered in more detail in chapter 7.

There must be an abundant source of carboniferous matter on the surface of the planet to provide organic chemicals, the basis of living cells. We mentioned silicon as a possible alternative to carbon, but the vast number of useful compounds that we know can be made from carbon has not anywhere been duplicated by silicon. Some have been made in the laboratory, but they are not found in nature. That's evident from the fact that silicon is abundant on the earth (start with sand, SiO_2), but silicon-based organic-like molecules have not formed here. Silicon, however, does perform an important function for Spacecraft Earth as a structural element in many crustal minerals. Silicate rocks make up some 90% of earth's crust, providing a firm continental foundation for plants and animals.

As we consider the many important features that support our life-friendly spacecraft, such as the presence near the surface of trace elements used by cells, these pile on the requirements for any exoplanet to be seriously considered a candidate for life. Let's recap just a few of the features that are absolutely essential for even simple life (ignoring the question of how life started even if all the physical requirements are met, a matter we will consider in chapter 5), and calculate the probability that all these characteristics will be found at a remote planet.

To put some numbers, say there are 100 billion galaxies, and each has 100 billion stars, that is 10^{22} stars. Let's say that one in 10,000 is a

G2 main-sequence star like our sun. That amounts to 10^{18} stars. Let's say that one in 10,000 of these stars has a planet in the habitable zone; that now gives us 10^{14} candidate planets. Let's further grant a generous 10% chance that any of the required features would 'happen' to be present in any one planet (I think a 1% chance would even be high). Everything has to be present simultaneously for there to be any chance of complex life existing. Some of the factors below are listed in the documentary *The Privileged Planet*, mentioned earlier.

Located within the galaxy habitable zone	10%
A stable star with constant energy output	10%
A planet formed within the habitable zone around the star	10%
A planet in a stable orbit maintaining a steady distance from the star	10%
Protected by gas giant planets in the solar system	10%
A rotation speed of about 24 hours	10%
A planet with a suitable atmosphere: oxygen rich, depth, circulation	10%
A planet with the appropriate mass	10%
A planet with abundant water	10%
A reasonable ratio of water to land mass	10%
A crust capable of plate tectonics	10%
A magnetic field within the proper strength range	10%
A moon of the proper size, distance, and orbit around the planet	10%
A readily available source of abundant carbon compounds	10%
Trace elements of the right type and quantity	10%

One could go on and on, adding more factors, but these are a few of the essential features to consider.

So let's multiply that out: $0.1 \times 0.1 \times 0.1 \times 0.1 \times 0.1 \times 0.1 \times 0.1 \times 0.1 \times 0.1 \times 0.1 \times 0.1 \times 0.1 \times 0.1 \times 0.1 \times 0.1 = 10^{-15}$. This probability times 10^{14} candidate planets leaves 10^{-1} planets, less than one!

Beyond that, if a habitable planet did exist somewhere, could we expect undirected evolution to once again bring about anything on the level of the beauty and complexity of life we find here on Spacecraft Earth? I maintain that it could not have happened once by accidental means here, much less than a second time elsewhere.

In review, we have considered just a few examples of factors from both extremes of scale—the astronomical and atomic—that make Spacecraft Earth an ideal habitat for life. Some of these factors, while not essential to life (like solar eclipses) are amazing coincidences unique to earth. Others, like the properties of water, habitable zones, and temperatures, while not unique to earth, are perfectly realized at our home planet. When combined with the considerations of the human body that we will look at next, a collection of evidence is growing that surely must captivate one's attention. It was precisely these kinds of evidences that I had learned and taught as an instructor of chemistry and a rocket scientist that, over time, caused me to question the usual explanation about where it all came from and what it all meant.

ENDNOTES

1. Wieland, C., Air in the Balance, *Creation* **18**(3):10–11, June 1996, creation.com/air-in-the-balance.

2. Livingstone, *et al.*, Sun-as-a-Star Spectrum Variations 1974-2006, *Astrophys. J.* **657**:1137–1149, 2007, doi: 10.1086/511127.

3. The quest for inhabited habitable planets, 3 June 2014, phys.org/news/2014-06-quest-inhabited-habitable-planets.html, based on paper by Zuluaga *et al.*, The Habitable Zone of Inhabited Planets, 19 May 2014, arxiv.org/abs/1405.4576.

4. Stellar makeup impacts habitable zone evolution, 7 Sept 2012, phys.org/news/2012-09-stellar-makeup-impacts-habitable-zone.html.

5. Gonzalez, G. and Richards, J., *The Privileged Planet*, Regnery Publishing, ch. 1, 2004.

6. Illustra Media, *The Privileged Planet*, 2004. Viewable on youtube.com/illustra.

2

The Spacesuit: The Amazing Human Body

To sail the universe on Spacecraft Earth, we need to be properly equipped. And are we ever! The more I learn about it, think about it, and try to understand it, the more I am in awe of the human body. A textbook on anatomy describes the parts, while a textbook on physiology shows how they function. One only has to leaf through such textbooks to begin to grasp the astonishing complexity of the body's systems, their intricate designs, and the wonder of how they all work together. The wonder extends all the way down to the molecular level. As passengers on Spacecraft Earth, we should take a moment to understand our equipment. We will see that the closer we look at even the most mundane parts, the more we see layers upon layers of bewildering organization.

Digestion

Our travel equipment includes an input-output system for maintenance of all its parts. We begin this chapter considering digestion, the system for taking in nutrients and manipulating them into the components for our cells, tissues, and organs. It all starts at the tip of the tongue.

Saliva

We take for granted the saliva in our mouths. Sometimes we even spit it out! But we should understand all it does for us. This amazing fluid, secreted all day and night by the salivary glands, serves a variety of purposes. It begins the digestion of our food. It contains several key chemical electrolytes, which are important in the mouth as well as the rest of the digestive tract. It also contains several important enzymes that begin to break down proteins, fats, and sugars. We remember our parents' admonition: "Chew your food well!" Chewing breaks up food into smaller pieces that the saliva can reach, making it much easier for digestion to begin.

Lips

It's interesting that the moist inside of the mouth transitions to the drier external skin through the lips. It's not just by chance that we find lips beautiful. Integral to both speech and digestion, our lips provide the doorway for food to enter and for breath and the voice to exit, as well as a soft, flexible platform

Flickr / Shazeen Samad / SSH

Figure 2-1. **Multifaceted tool**
Human lips are integral to speech and digestion, among other things.

for the loving contact of a kiss. The inside edge of each lip consists of wet mucous membrane from the interior of the mouth. The outside of the lip contains the only semi-moist portion of our exterior skin. Because they are tied into multiple specialized muscles, the lips give us the ability to make dozens of facial expressions, and to pronounce hundreds of thousands of words (feel how they move precisely with the letters b, f, m, p, r, v, and w). Here is a multi-functional design that ties seamlessly into other multi-functional designs, like the saliva we are discussing.

Saliva continuously lubricates the mucous membranes inside the mouth. A mucous membrane is a special type of skin that coats the interior of the mouth and throat, preparing the food we have chewed to enter the digestive tract. We all know how uncomfortable a dry mouth feels! Thankfully, that feeling is rare, even in a desert environment, because of our always-functioning salivary glands.

Salivary glands

The glands that produce saliva are arranged in two sets of three, located in matching pairs on both sides of the mouth. We must remember that organs do not sit in isolation; they are linked to blood vessels and nerves, which are controlled by the brain. The salivary glands have to 'know' how to manufacture all the key enzymes in saliva, as well as how often to secrete them. Do not these six organs, arranged symmetrically inside the mouth, look well designed for their tasks (see Figure 2-2)?

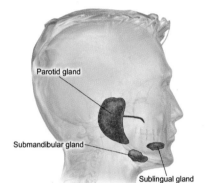

Figure 2-2. Salivary glands
Designed to secrete different types of saliva to aid in digestion

of Medicine. DOI:10.15347/wjm/2014.010. ISSN 20018762.

Swallowing

When we swallow, the food passes down the throat through the esophagus into the stomach. The throat, however, is also our windpipe. It's possible (but not polite) to talk and eat at almost the same time. By design, there is a valve (the epiglottis) that can switch rapidly between the two pipes. This valve works well most of the time, except every now and then when we are careless. If food or drink gets into the windpipe, though, there is safety response: the coughing reflex. It is usually effective, except in severe cases of choking, in which case we hope a friend knowing the Heimlich maneuver is nearby, able to press the air in the lungs into service to forcefully expel the food back out. When we chew our food and eat properly, though, such experiences are rare. A nonagenarian like me has swallowed millions of times without a thought. No man-made valve has that kind of performance record.

Now, how did this dual function tube and valve process develop? Think about it; which came first: the swallowing part or the breathing part? In a complex mechanism such as this, did evolution create two separate tubes, which somehow fused? How would it work before the valve came into being? The system only works when all the parts are present, functioning as a unit. When we breathe through the nose, the valve operates automatically to allow air to enter and leave the lungs.

We can also breathe through the mouth. The valve anticipates both actions correctly. We can quickly swallow saliva between breaths, and again the valve functions automatically to direct the right connection to the right tube, very rapidly, without our conscious thought. This dual function system is but one of several in the human body.

Digestive juices

Let us look at the chemistry of digestion. The alimentary canal starts at the mouth, continues through the pharynx, esophagus, stomach, duodenum, small intestines, colon, and rectum, ending at the anus. Throughout this canal numerous digestive juices are produced to break down our food into its basic building blocks that the body can use to construct muscle, bone, and all the tissues of the body. In the mouth, our teeth (a glistening toolkit of ceramic cutters and grinders with different shapes), cut, crush and grind the food into small particles. How convenient that teeth are right there at the entrance to the mouth! Simultaneously, saliva is poured into the mouth from our three pairs of salivary glands, named the parotid, submandibular and sublingual. The parotid gland secretes clear saliva, the other two a sticky saliva containing mucin. The saliva moistens the food so that it can be rolled by the tongue and palate into a soft bolus. When the food is sufficiently masticated, it is pushed backwards by the tongue into the pharynx where the swallowing reflex causes a series of muscular movements, called peristalsis. This propels the food into the esophagus, and thence into the stomach.

Saliva contains a multitude of chemical salts and enzymes, many of which are probably still undiscovered. An enzyme called ptyalin breaks down starch into maltose, a simple sugar. Another enzyme, amylase, also converts starch into sugars. Lysozyme, discovered by Scottish bacteriologist Sir Alexander Fleming in 1922, is an antibacterial enzyme present in saliva, nasal secretions, and tears. It has the ability to break down the cell walls of bacteria, helping sterilize our food before it enters the digestive tract. This enzyme is of historical interest. While studying lysozyme, Fleming found an unusual mold growing on a neglected culture dish. He isolated this mold and grew it into a pure culture; this led to his discovery of penicillin. In 1945, he shared the Nobel Prize in Physiology or Medicine for this major discovery that opened the door for the widespread application of antibiotics for disease control.

Already, we see that one of the most ordinary things about our body, saliva (sometimes denigrated as 'spit') is anything but simple. It contains complex molecules. It breaks down food and acts as a disinfectant. It is produced by glands that are arranged precisely in the mouth. It moistens the lips, the palate, and the upper digestive tract. And it is tied into other systems that are even more complex. Today, many are taught that saliva, with all its functions and inter-connections, originated by blind, unguided processes of evolution. Does it seem reasonable that these systems began as small mistakes in pre-existing systems? All those systems would also have originated by mistake. It would be mistakes all the way down!

A gland might start by some aberrant development of a few cells. But to be useful as a secretory organ, this precursor gland would have to have its own blood supply, so more genetic mistakes would have to generate blood vessels off of the main circulatory system. How would these precursor glands exist and prosper before the blood vessels developed? In addition, the salivary glands are controlled by special nerves out of the brain. (These command the increased flow and change in composition of saliva, for instance, when you see a juicy steak.) How could imaginary precursor glands improve the fitness of an organism before they had blood vessels and nerves? How did the new information get passed on into the gametes so that the next generation would benefit?

Keep in mind that the evolution of saliva had to occur in the same population at the same time that all manner of other evolu-tionary advances were supposedly emerging, as we shall see. It's incomprehensible enough, just for the salivary system, to imagine mistakes getting it right. How many of thousands upon thousands of generations would be required for enough random mistakes to occur before the system worked? Would 'sheer dumb luck' create glands in matched symmetrical pairs, with their discharge tubes aimed into the mouth, their nerve activators extending to the precise part of the brain that delicately controls their every action twenty four hours a day, every day from the moment of birth? Where did the information come from to produce the enzymes, exactly the ones needed to break down food, with exactly the right alkalinity and concentration? How could an organism function or exist before all this physiology was put into place?

Teeth

Teeth are another example of functional design. They are attached to a movable lower jaw (the mandible) and to a protrusion of the skull (the maxilla). All humans have the same number and varieties of teeth from front to back—again, in matching pairs. It is interesting to note that teeth have different functions, starting with the biting, cutting edge of the incisors in front to the grinding action of the molars in back.

It is also interesting to note how two different sets of teeth emerge during childhood. The temporary 'baby teeth' emerge first, and then these fall out and are replaced by the adult or permanent teeth during childhood. What kind of random evolutionary process could produce this double crop of teeth?

Another difference between human teeth and those of other vertebrates is seen in so-called canine teeth. Also called the cuspid, eye-tooth, or dog-tooth, the canine has only one 'cusp' or point. Growing into position beside the incisors (front teeth), our matching canines are single-rooted teeth used for tearing food. These are often the largest teeth in the mouth. In non-human species, the canines project well beyond the level of the other teeth, and may interlock when the mouth is closed, restricting the animal to an up-and-down chewing action. Among sheep, oxen and deer, only the upper canines are large, while the lower ones resemble incisors.

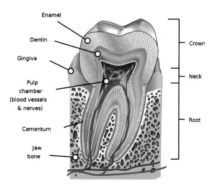

Enamel
Dentin
Gingiva
Pulp chamber (blood vessels & nerves)
Cementum
Jaw bone

Crown
Neck
Root

Figure 2-3. Inside a human tooth
Molars, like this, are designed for grinding, while incisors are made for cutting.

The tusks of wild boar, walrus, and the extinct saber-tooth cat are enlarged canines. In some animals (e.g., pig, deer, baboon, and gorilla), the male has much larger canines than does the female; these perform a threatening and protective function besides that of tearing. (Note: the tusks of elephants are upper incisors, not canine teeth; they have no canines.) The teeth of dolphins, by contrast, all look alike. The way they are aligned at a specific angle in the snout leads some researchers to hypothesize that they may act as antennas, enhancing sonar reception in echolocation.

Humans have small canines that do not project beyond the level of the other teeth—thus, in humans alone, among the primates, rotary chewing action is possible. In humans there are four canines, one on each side of each jaw. Here is another significant departure between the human species and non-human primates. In apes, further, the jaw is U-shaped, rather than the curved V-shape of humans. Fossil hunters can tell the difference easily.

The structure of a tooth itself shows intricate design. For example, the enamel covering of a typical tooth is composed of prismatic rods of crystal apatite, making it the hardest tissue in the body. It is highly resistant to chemical and physical weathering or attack, and it has an automatic repair process. When minor cracks called 'tufts' appear in the dentin or enamel, protein fills in the cracks, making it more resistant to further cracking. How interesting it is that tooth enamel exists at all! If enamel developed as part of an evolutionary process, how did unprotected teeth survive beforehand?

Nutrition

Let's consider the ultimate purpose of saliva and teeth: nutrition. Food is the fuel for our vehicles. It provides energy, builds cells and tissues, and, as a bonus, gives us pleasure. We are fortunate that our planet produces abundantly for our nutritional needs, if we take responsibility for eating the right substances. Both plant and animal tissues provide food for us, and what a variety! The food we eat (and obviously need for survival) is both quite simple and quite sophisticated. At the elemental level, there are some 28 chemical elements required in the human body. In most places on Spacecraft Earth, fortunately, they are abundant near the surface. At the molecular level, food can be classified into proteins, carbohydrates, and fats. Along with these are a very necessary collection of vitamins and minerals.

In order to get proper nutrition, we need all of the above. We cannot thrive on just protein, just carbohydrate, or just fat. Remember the tales of seafaring men who developed scurvy from not having vitamin C? Once they learned to eat limes and lemons aboard ship, the symptoms disappeared. We still see sad evidences of malnutrition around our world in pictures from poor countries. Obtaining the right nutritional elements is fundamental to good health and growth. Without going into overmuch detail, let's think about a few aspects of good nutrition, starting with vitamins and minerals.

Vitamins

A dozen or so primary vitamins are recognized, and each plays a role in different physiological processes. Vitamins are, as the name implies, 'vital' for facilitating body functions and growth, but they are primarily produced by plants. What causes a plant to produce vitamins for the benefit of humans? There is something in the genetic makeup of plants that drives them to synthesize vitamins: indeed, plants are incomparable masters of organic chemistry, producing many thousands of 'phytochemicals' (plant molecules) that benefit animals as well as themselves. Many plant species produce unique vitamins. What in the process of undirected evolution would result in such prodigious molecular output for the benefit of animals that eat what plants make? Vitamins do not seem to be important for the survival of the plants that produce them. How could evolution tie a plant's synthesis of vitamins, involving many precise steps of manufacture that organic chemists find challenging, to the needs of an animal body?

The production of vitamin C, for example, does not result from just a single gene in plant DNA. A plant follows a precise script to manufacture vitamin C. Building block molecules must be manufactured first. Then vitamin C is synthesized by combining the building blocks in an exact way, just like an organic chemist does in a lab. How could each step in this process develop in synchrony to end up with the right chemical structure? Consider, too, that many different plant species are necessary for the suite of vitamins that we need. Did the right 'mistakes' happen in many different plants independently and simultaneously?

Minerals

Next are the minerals that we need for health and growth. Some minerals we use in large quantities, and fortuitously these occur in large amounts on the earth. Take salt for example: we need salt to support electrolyte levels in our blood and other body fluids. Our bodies are able to regulate the amount of salt that goes into these various fluids, and although this may seem like a minor function, an electrolyte imbalance can be fatal. Animals regulate their salt in various ways, each of them tightly controlled. Salmon, for instance, are able to switch the cells in their gills from excreting salt in the ocean to absorbing it in the fresh water as they swim upstream to their breeding grounds, where salt is much less abundant.

In addition to the major minerals we need, such as salt as an electrolyte, and iron to help the blood transport oxygen, there are a host of others that we need in minute quantities. We've all seen mineral supplements in stores that advertise copper, selenium, zinc chromium, molybdenum, manganese and others. These are only trace elements in the body, but are important to good health. Fortunately, these exist in sufficient quantities on our earth. Most healthy people get sufficient quantities from food. Here's a question to ponder: did our bodies learn to assimilate and use these trace minerals, or do they exist because our bodies need them? The answer is that complex life could probably not exist without them. Recently, for instance, scientists at Vanderbilt University announced that "without bromine, there are no animals."[1] Bromine is not found in the bodies of animals, but it plays a critical role during one step in the formation of tissues like collagen. Even fruit flies without bromine in their diet could not survive. Manganese is found in our bones, liver, kidneys and brains; plants use it to efficiently split water into hydrogen and oxygen. We only need about 12 micrograms (millionths of a gram) but could not live without it. What if our planet did not have this trace element readily available? It appears that the design of our planet is intricately linked to the design of its lifeforms.

Nourishing the young

All higher forms of life need to protect, nourish and educate their young. Asexual organisms, like the amoeba, simply divide, go off on their own and grow. Invertebrate egg-laying animals such as spiders lay eggs that are on their own after they hatch. Because large numbers of eggs are produced (with only a few surviving), their species continue to propagate.

Even the progeny of some egg-laying vertebrate animals, such as turtles and snakes, go their own way after hatching, and instinctively know how to find food, eat and fend for themselves. However, the highest forms of life, particularly the birds and mammals, produce young which are incapable of surviving on their own. They require nourishment and protection by their parents for a period of their young lives.

As with all mammals, human mothers produce a nourishing food called milk. Milk is carefully crafted to provide for all of the needs of infants until they are sufficiently developed to ingest other liquid and solid foods. All mammals produce milk, but there is quite a difference between human milk and other types of milk, such as cow's milk.

The female breast has glands that produce milk only under certain conditions. The mammary (milk-producing) glands start their production toward the end of pregnancy, and continue only long enough to produce milk for the appropriate time of weaning the young. Then milk production ceases. It would be an outstanding evolutionary happenstance to not only develop glands that produce milk on a very specialized schedule, but to also produce milk with just the right ingredients for another individual—the baby.

Pexels.com

Figure 2-4. Food for thought
Breast milk supplies nutrition and antibodies to help babies fight infections, and is programmed to change over time.

Milk is an emulsion of fat globules in a colloidal suspension of protein together with other substances in solution. Two constituents of milk—the protein casein and the sugar lactose—are not found elsewhere in the body. Breast milk contains significant nutritional factors (vitamins, minerals and protein) and anti-infectious factors. These are enhanced by the very action of breast feeding which has psychological as well as nutritional benefits. Human breast milk is superior to modified cow's milk formulas or the milk from other mammals because the latter lack essential and beneficial components needed by human babies. They are also not absorbed as easily or as quickly by the infant. Only human maternal breast milk provides the right balance of vitamins, minerals, protein, and anti-infectious factors a baby needs; it also supplies antibodies that protect the infant's newly-formed gastrointestinal tract, resulting in a lower rate of enteric infection in breast-fed babies. Amazingly, mother's milk contains some sugars that only beneficial bacteria can digest, showing that the milk actually primes the supply of normal flora in the baby's digestive tract while protecting against harmful bacteria. One surprised researcher said that it's like "Mother is recruiting another life form to babysit her baby."[2]

Another marvel is that breast milk changes during weaning. Programmed instructions modify milk at appropriate stages, from colostrum to transitional milk to mature milk. Studies have shown that breast milk, even from a donor, is the best way for premature infants to gain fat. Breast-fed infants also have lower rates of infection. Human milk has an optimal concentration of omega-3 fatty acids to promote brain development. Lactation also has benefits for the mother. Studies have shown a decreased risk of cancer for those who had breastfed their babies.[3]

Clearly, breastfeeding with natural mother's milk best meets the needs for the growth and development of the baby and is healthy for the mother, too. This was particularly true before recent civilization produced its plethora of infant-feeding concoctions. If there was an early evolutionary form of humans in which the complexities of milk did not yet exist, then the survival of the infant would be severely challenged. It is unlikely the species would survive, much less propagate.

Mother's milk has so many different constituents, the spontaneous development of all of these at one time is highly unlikely. Similarly, the development of the breast structure and function in adult women would also require a multitude of evolutionary changes. As mentioned, the human breast structure and milk composition is quite different from that of other mammals, particularly apes and monkeys. Trying to imagine a series of unplanned random mutations getting it all together when it's needed requires more faith than getting the design right from the beginning. This is just one more 'simple' example illustrating how many independent factors would have had to come together simultaneously in order to produce the human body from something else. As we have seen, this one example is anything but simple! Keep in mind what we already said about saliva, digestion, and nutrition. The human body stands as a completed creation: marvelously self-sustaining, self-repairing, highly functional, and beautiful.

Mechanical engineering

The elbow

The elbow is a marvelous piece of mechanical design. It is an articulating joint between two bone structures that allows movement of the arm along two different axes (hinge movement and some rotation). An elbow is essential for people to be able to manipulate their surroundings. It's just one example of the hundreds of

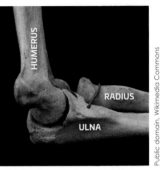

Figure 2-5. **Human elbow**
Showing bones and ball/socket joint

joints in the human body. Fingers have three joints each. The wrists have gliding joints that allow motions in two dimensions, allowing the hand to move up and down or side to side. The shoulders have ball-and-socket joints. The legs have joints at the hips, knees, and ankles. Feet have dozens of joints; the bone structure of the foot is "a biomechanical masterpiece" one news report said.[4]

The elbow is a 'hinge joint' that connects the humerus of the upper arm to the radius and ulna of the forearm. It actually consists of three joints in one. The humeroradial joint is a 'ball and socket' joint that complements the hinge-type humeroulnar joint. The bone ball is perfectly matched to the cavity of the socket. Cushioned with cartilage, it permits smooth, easy movement while being held in place in this captured position. Cartilage provides a gentle, very low friction surface between the ball and the socket. Then there is a gland, which secretes the perfect lubricant to the cartilage, thus ensuring low friction between the ball and the socket. Figure 2-5 shows the basic components.

We must wonder, again, how all these parts could have come together through a series of random mistakes (mutations). If they required numerous small, gradual changes one-by-one, then how did rudimentary bone joints function before all of the necessary features were in place and working in concert? How could a mutation creating a ball provide any fitness benefit before its matching socket arrived? A square ball and a square socket certainly wouldn't work. If the first production of a ball at the end of the bone was not approximately spherical, then how could the joint move? If the joint didn't move, it would be useless, and the survivability of the body would be very much in question. If the first product of an elbow were so crude as to not allow much movement, then how did that body survive and produce countless generations in order to let random chance produce a more perfect joint?

The elbow is not only able to bend like a hinge, but also to rotate in the upper radius-ulnar joint, rotating the hand with it. This requires an additional set of muscles, the radius bone fitting into the socket and controlling the ball at the end of the humerus bone. That's amazing.

The same can be said for all the other articulating joints in the body. It is interesting to me that all of the joints are so similar in function and design. If an elbow came about through a long chain of random, gradual variations to individual elements, then how come our two elbows are identical, yet mirror images of each other? If one of them developed through a long series of spontaneous aberrations, it seems remarkable that an identical set of aberrations would have happened to the other elbow to create an identical design with the opposite orientation. Even if, (as evolutionists believe), these came about by master-switch genes far upstream of the details, why would these master switches create symmetry between left and right parts of the body?

Consider just one elbow. How could it develop without fore-thought, having to simultaneously produce a bone ball and match-ing socket, the cartilage just right to cushion movement, and the lubricating fluid to maintain the cartilage? Each is necessary for the proper working of the whole. If any one of these elements was missing or improperly shaped, that early organism would have had a very difficult time of movement and survival waiting for random chance, again through countless generations, to supply the missing cartilage, fluid or exact matching shape of the ball and socket.

That lubricating fluid, by the way, has been called 'nature's most effective grease.' The substance, called lubricin, is a protein with tiny 'feet' that attach themselves to virtually any surface. The proteins assemble into a dense, carpet-like layer between the joints that cushions the bones as well as reducing friction as they slide past one another. Without this amazing substance, bones would wear out much faster and our movements would be painful and stiff. Instead, they allow us to operate like a 'well-oiled machine'. Was the origin of this highly effective lubricant just one more accident of nature?

We do not see imperfect or missing forms around us now, except in rare circumstances—and those are usually caused by genetic defects. Yet genetic defects are supposed to be the raw material for improvement in living things! Genetic defects are overwhelmingly deleterious. Even if a beneficial mutation did arise, it would not add novel genetic information which is required for organisms to progress from simple to complex. Most likely, it would be useless (and quickly removed) if the matching parts had not arrived by another mistake in the same individual in a population.

The same series of questions can be asked about the dozens of other joints in our elbows, knees, hips, fingers, and toes. It is certainly interesting that all of them are identical in design but come in mirror-image pairs.

Similarly, think of the spine, with its capability to move up and down along most of its length. The spinal joints between vertebrae display a different design altogether. Being hollow, they provide a protective conduit for the nerves. It would be bad news if our nerves ran outside the protection of the spine! But protected inside, they allow signals to pass from the brain down the neck, through the vertebrae, and then throughout the body, all the way to the ends of the fingers and toes. It's an absolutely marvelous piece of design engineering! To appreciate its design specs, consider the jumping, turning, twisting and contorting movements of Olympic athletes, particularly the gymnasts. How did random mutations achieve this level of performance?

The foot

The complexity of the bone structure of the foot was mentioned in the prior section. All mammals have four limbs, always developed in identical mirror-image pairs. Land-dwelling mammals have feet (or paws) for support, locomotion, and manipulation of objects.

The human foot has much more than a set of good bones. Their interconnections and operations require an intricate set of joints, cartilage, muscles, nerves and tendons joining muscle to bone. Injury to any of these operational elements can cause pain and dysfunction, but in many cases, are self-healing. A comprehensive nerve network signals internal injury or trauma with the pain reflex. This is undoubtedly a protective function to protect an injured foot against additional trauma or aggravation of injury.

Once again, we should ponder how this complex system arose. Think of the design requirements. You would need muscles of the correct size and location to operate all of the bones and joints in the foot. You would need nerves in the right locations, able to send sensations of pleasure or pain. These nerves would have to know how to operate the muscles, making them contract or relax. Nerves, remember, are not just little localized fibers. They consist of very long single cells that connect each location to specific sites in the spinal cord, and then to the brain. The individual nerves, furthermore, need to come together in a nerve bundle that passes through the protective hollow vertebral bones. Complex requirements like these are never met by a series of small, gradual mistakes. Systems of systems that work together are hallmarks of masterful engineering.

We know that the nerve function is vital to the operation of a foot, and so how did that foot even function before the requisite nerve appeared? Or, did the nerves appear before the muscles? What causative action would create a nerve before it had a function? In order for muscles to perform their work, they are connected by tendons to the bones to cause movement. Which came first, muscles, tendons, or nerves? These are all separate types of body structures, composed of separate kinds of cells, tissues and organs. It would not be expected, in my thinking, that chance mutations would create even two of these simultaneously. No amount of time would be sufficient.

Then again, there comes the matter of humans having two identical, mirror-image feet. There is no reason to believe that any mutational change in an organism happens in such a way as to create identical pairs of integrated structures composed of multiple independent parts. An upstream genetic 'switch' might create two left feet, but not a right and left. And it could only switch on what already existed downstream.

The human foot consists of twenty-six bones all working in concert. Figure 2-6 depicts the bone structure of a human foot. This does not show the intricacy and interrelationship of all of the bones, muscles, tendons, nerves and blood vessels. Oh, yes, let's talk about blood vessels! A newly created muscle tissue is not going to do well without a blood supply. This is mandatory for supplying oxygen, bringing in nutrients for growth, removing the waste products of metabolism, repairing damage, fighting infections, and much more. In Figure 2-6, notice that at the top there are grooves where the tendons fit in. If early evolutionary mutations developed bones without those grooves for the tendons, the tendons would have been exposed to injury.

If you think back to my discussion in the prior section about the elbow, now we come to a structure that has, in essence, twenty 'elbows' that must function perfectly. Each joint between the foot bones has a ball-and-socket structure as part of the bone itself. Each movable joint has built-in cartilage, lubrication glands, muscles and tendons—all finely tuned and synchronized to allow movement. Now, I am not aware of even one joint in the foot that has yet to have cartilage added to it. Everything is complete; there is no part waiting for some other part to appear by mutational mistake. How fortuitous for us! All of these joints (in both feet!) are a finished product working essentially perfectly, not lacking anything needed for standing, walking, and running. Mutations only cause defects—not improvements—to this finely-tuned system.

Frequently, as I am standing in one place, or perhaps bracing myself into a wind, I marvel at the miracle of being able to stand upright. This is possible only through a foot that has sufficient internal movement and reaction to allow us to balance on these two stilts we call legs. Standing still is a dynamic process! The brain has sensors and a servo control system that constantly monitors the position of each joint in each foot, switching on the appropriate foot and leg muscles for each slight shift of position. As a result, we can

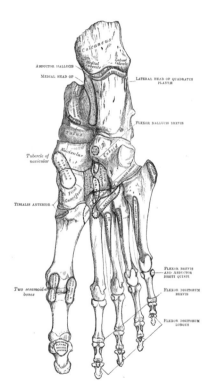

Figure 2-6. **Human foot bones**

defy gravity, maintaining balance in a standing position. Without all these systems working together, we would quickly collapse into a heap on the ground. The systems appear even more marvelous when you consider walking or running. Picture a boy hopping from rock to rock in a stream. The eyes, brain, nerves, and muscles are all responding with split-second timing to keep him upright as he makes constant decisions where to place his foot next, even though the rocks are not level and might be slick. It would be a major project to design a robot able to do that.

This small book could easily expand into an encyclopedia were we to consider all the different actions and control functions directed by the brain, be they standing, walking, running, talking, blinking our eyes, breathing, and the thousands of other activities of which we are capable. Often we engage in several activities at the same time, like when talking on a cell phone while walking, or when engaging our entire bodies in sports. There are many additional activities the brain takes care of without our conscious thought, like breathing, digesting food, and controlling heartbeats. The brain's command and control center operates on electricity with the power of a 100-watt light bulb. (We can see our 'body electricity' in the way electrical impulses of a certain frequency can cause a muscle to contract or relax.) An electric potential is set up by nano-sized machines in neurons that pump sodium and potassium ions in and out of the membranes. As a wave train passes, the ions exchange places then quickly reset. At the junctions of nerve endings, called synapses, the electrical signal is converted into chemical signals (neurotransmitters) that travel across a small gap to the next neuron in small packages called vesicles. Upon receipt of the vesicle, the neuron re-converts the chemical energy to electrical energy. The electrical impulses travel not only to the extremities, but back again, supplying the brain with updated information on each joint and muscle. This all happens ultra-fast (think of that child hopping rocks, or a sprinter in a race). It's only in recent decades that these tiny mechanical processes in neurons have come to light.

Now, back to the foot. Figure 2-6 showed the primary structure of a human foot. Figure 2-7 compares the shapes of an ape foot and a human foot. Many believe that apes are the ancestors of humans. Although there are some similarities in bone structure and operation, the human foot is a radically different design. The ape foot has different structures, sizes, and shapes of bones. The exterior of the foot is much different as can be seen from the figure. The numbers of bones are different, the shapes are different, and the design is different. If evolution produced the human foot from an ape foot, the differences are not simple modifications from one form to another but more like a new design from scratch. Otherwise, we would have to account for literally thousands of upgrades in functionality.

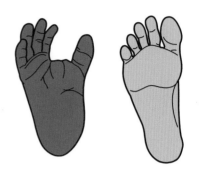

Figure 2-7. **Chimpanzee vs. human foot**

The ape foot is intended for a much different environment. True, apes can walk upright for short distances, but their foot structure is much better suited to climbing trees and knuckle-walking along the ground.

The shape of the human foot is much different, clearly adapted for walking upright all of the time. It has a unique bone structure, muscle structure, and sole, with two arches almost perpendicular to each other. The heel and ankle are suited to living on the ground, not in the trees. What chance mutations created such a radical change? Evolutionists often gloss over these details, simply imagining that a change in climate led some ape ancestor to climb out of the trees and start walking. Such things do not just happen. There would be too many things for natural selection to do at the same time.

And, of course, the parallel question again comes: if we came from apes, how did this set of changes occur simultaneously with all of the other supposed upgrades, such as the brain structure and functionality, the jaw conversion, or the development of a skin with just a minor amount of fine hair instead of the hairy ape look, a throat and mouth structure that allows speech, and so on. These are not 'upgrade' level changes that occurred in a variety of different individuals but major redesigns, which all have to have happened in concert in a common ancestor. The mathematical probability of a mutation leading to any one redesign is infinitesimally small, let alone the thousands that would have been needed together.

Defense: the immune system

Another very important feature of the human body—something vital for long, healthy life—is the immune system. This multi-part system defends us from biotic invasions, but distinguishes between 'friendly' bacteria that help digest food in our guts and harmful ones that cause disease. The devastating effects of acquired immune deficiency syndrome (AIDS) and other conditions that suppress or destroy parts of our immunity show what can happen when this system is compromised.

The adaptive immune system is found only in vertebrates. This complicated system has multiple components, which include antigens, antibodies, and various types of blood cells such as B and T lymphocytes. The collective interaction of these components results in a coordinated, multi-level response to infectious organisms. Antigens are things that trigger an immune response. They might be proteins, polysaccharides (complex carbohydrates), or foreign substances, including molecules found in bacteria, viruses and fungi, or substances that mark the surface of cells with foreign materials such as pollen or transplanted tissue.

When antigens are detected, the body goes to work producing custom antibodies to fight them. Antibodies, or immunoglobulins, are proteins directed against specific antigens; they are formed in the lymph nodes or bone marrow by mature D lymphocytes called plasma cells. These are placed into circulation throughout the body to bind and neutralize antigens wherever they are found. This type of response, called humoral immunity, is mainly against toxins and free pathogens (those not ingested by phagocytes) in body fluids.

A second type of response, called cell-mediated immunity, does not produce antibodies, but instead triggers the production of T lymphocytes, which act against specific threats. T cells are able to neutralize bacteria, fungi, cancer cells, transplanted tissue cells, and cells that have been invaded by viruses. In each case, the immune response prevents the invaders from causing further damage to the host. As if that were not enough, there's another immune response called the complement system. This is composed of a group of proteins circulating in the blood. They facilitate the immune response in two ways: by attracting phagocytes ('eating cells') to the area so that they can swallow the invaders, and by forming a protein complex that attaches to the foreign cell, causing lysis (splitting, or death) of the invaders.

Two remarkable qualities of our immune system are its specificity and memory. When an antigen enters a body, it elicits production of either a specific antibody or specific immunologically competent cells; that is, the antibody or the cells will neutralize only the antigen that evokes them. Furthermore, the system exhibits what appears to be memory. Once challenged by an antigen such as the measles virus, the body 'remembers' it for years and usually for life. The child who has had an attack of measles becomes permanently immune to it. If the child is exposed to this specific antigen at a later date, the immune system recognizes it and responds, and thereby prevents a reinfection. Indeed, these two characteristics of the immune system—specificity and memory—serve as the basis for preventive immunizations. Inoculation of infants or children with an inactivated or attenuated biotic agent will cause the immune system to be made alert to such an antigen, should it appear at a later date. Poliomyelitis, for example, once dreaded as a leading cause of paralysis and death, has been effectively controlled, if not abolished, with the polio vaccine, at least in most developed countries.

Medical science and physiological research has barely begun to understand all of the facets of the human immune system. We surely could not survive without it. Of the body systems we've examined so far, it's a great example of multiple, disparate parts working together in harmony. It could not have arrived piecemeal. A phagocyte that can 'eat' another cell would be a monster if not responsive to a signal transduction system that tells it what to attack. A thymus gland that can match antibodies to antigens would be useless if other parts of the system did not recognize the antibodies in order to attach to infected cells and destroy them. The lymph nodes, the marrow within our bones that produce blood cells, the specific

Pexels.com

Figure 2-8. **Human eyebrows**
Good at keeping water and dust out of our eyes, but are they really necessary for survival?

enzymes that circulate in blood and lymph, and a host of other things are all involved together, each one necessary to make the immune system work. Thankfully, everything is there that is necessary, and the system usually works very well.

Decoration: eyebrows and facial hair

Here's another mundane part of our anatomy that can be easily taken for granted. Human beings have two eyebrows, symmetrically placed above the eyes, usually with a gap between. If a mutation produced some dark hairs above an individual's eyes, why did it stop with that particular shape and size? Eyebrows are attractive, and they offer a bit of protection from dust falling into the eyes from above, but they don't seem to offer a significant reproductive advantage. Why would 'survival of the fittest' select an eyebrowed individual over one not so decorated?

Figure 2-9. **Non-essential attributes**
What is the purpose of a beard beyond decoration and distinguishing between men and women?

Similarly, a beard on a mature male is not vital for survival, as many men shave theirs off. Why does it grow on certain parts of the face, and not others? Why does it grow on men, and not women? Why does it grow on men and not boys? Some monkeys have beards or moustaches, like the emperor tamarin, but these usually grow on both sexes. Natural selection should eliminate any trait that expends energy but does not aid survival. In fact, to perpetuate a trait, evolutionary theory requires that everyone without the trait must die. This is called the 'cost of selection'. Are eyebrows, eyelashes, beards, and other non-essential traits so important to survival that everyone without them had to perish? This makes no sense.

The windows: vision

One of my favorite topics is vision. There are at least half a dozen (if not hundreds) of independent developments that would need to come together to create the human eye. Yes, evolutionists can line up a series of eyes in a putative sequence, from primitive light-sensitive spots in some lower animals, increasing in complexity through invertebrates, fish, and tetrapods. This simplistic sequence, though, glosses over the fact that complex eyes appear suddenly in the fossil record—in trilobites, for instance. Another evolutionary conundrum is why squid and octopus, which bear no relationship to humans in the evolutionary ancestral scheme, have camera-like

Figure 2-10. **Trilobite eye**

eyes of comparable complexity to ours. Additionally, the number of exceptional adaptations in the mammalian eye are so over-the-top sophisticated, they approach design perfection. For these and other

Figure 2-11. **Squid eye**

reasons, evolutionists are in no position to argue for gradual development of the eye by a blind, aimless Darwinian mechanism.

Let us begin with the eye itself. Like a video camera, it has a window that takes in light, focuses it with a lens, then projects it onto a sensor panel, the retina. (By the way, camera manufacturers are just now recognizing the superior optical performance of a curved sensor.)[5] Numerous muscles move the eyeball and lens, keeping the image centered and in focus; both eyeballs move in a coordinated fashion faster than the blink of an eye.

On the retina, the focused light activates chemicals in the rods and cones, converting the electromagnetic energy into chemical energy. The chemical energy, in turn, converts the image into electrical energy in the optic nerve, where it travels

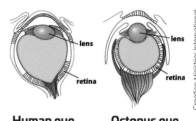

Human eye   **Octopus eye**

Figure 2-12.

down neuron cells to the vision center in the brain, the visual cortex. The electrical signals are processed by the brain, turning what began as photons into a moving picture we recognize. During each energy conversion, there is essentially zero loss. We can perceive, in ideal situations, single photons of light.[6]

Each one of these components has many sub-components, all of which have to function simultaneously. The eye has a clear lens at the proper distance at the rear of the eye to form an image of the scene before it. It has muscles that are able to change the focal length to allow focusing from examining the small portion of a person's finger looking for a splinter to gazing at the distant stars in the sky. The eye is filled with a vitreous fluid that has the exact index of refraction required to match the focal characteristics of the lens, forming an image at the precise location where the retina is.

Then there is the retina itself that consists of millions of rods and cones. In these specialized cells, a protein named rhodopsin responds to light by changing conformations extremely rapidly and back again. These atomic-scale changes are picked up and transmitted to the nerves as electrical impulses. Recently, biologists discovered that special cells in the retina, called Müller cells, act as waveguides, directing single photons directly to the rods and cones with perfect efficiency. These Müller cells are analogous to the waveguides we designed in the radio antennas for NASA's Deep Space Network to pick up faint signals from space. Little did we know that there were waveguides right inside our eyeballs!

Consider the optic nerve, which consists of a closely spaced bundle of biologically active electrical conductors that pass electrical impulses along very rapidly, using electrochemical reactions. They are not metallic wires, but, instead are long cells with specialized membrane transport portals like the ones we discussed earlier. Arranged in series, they pump potassium and sodium ions in and out, very rapidly, like a wave traveling down the nerve fiber. Between each neuron, that energy is reconverted to chemical energy by neurotransmitters—using the vesicles mentioned earlier—then back to electrical energy in the next neuron. This all happens so fast we think we see the world in 'real time' which is very close to the truth.

We could go on and on talking just about the eye. How could eyes work without a skull with eye sockets built in, just the right size? How could they work without conduits for the nerves passing through the skull at the right point to reach the visual cortex in the brain? A million accidental mutations could not begin to account for this level of sophisticated design.

Could the eye evolve?

Evolutionists, though, expect us to believe that such a system came about by random, accidental changes to an organism without eyes, or with primitive eyes. I suppose it is possible that some cells on the surface of an organism might develop some type of sensitivity to light. We are familiar with the fact that our skin has sensitivity to sunlight independent of our eyes. A pigment called melanin responds by darkening the skin slowly over a period of sun exposure. Presumably, the primitive organism evolving the first eye would be responsive only to light or dark to begin with. That sensitivity, though, would be useless without an independent neural system able to use that information. Notice that the neural system would need those membrane portals and vesicles to work, requiring many prior mutations. But the primitive neural system, in turn, would be useless without the ability to respond by sending signals to a primitive muscular system. Here we see, once again, that a beneficial mutation for one thing confers no survival advantage without many other beneficial mutations occurring simultaneously in other parts of the organism. And that's just to get started with vision.

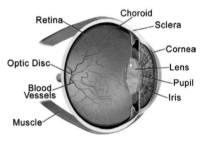

Figure 2-13. **Eye anatomy**

I have greatly oversimplified how vision works. What we've considered so far, though, brings up an important concept we need to consider. It's called 'irreducible complexity'. The term was coined by Dr Michael Behe[7], a biochemist at Lehigh University, after he became aware of molecular machines like the bacterial flagellum, described later. Thinking over the difficulties of arriving at complex molecular machines through a Darwinian process, he became increasingly dissatisfied with the standard explanations taught as fact—evolutionary explanations he never questioned through graduate school until some of the problems were pointed out to him by another molecular biologist. In his book *Darwin's Black Box*, where he gave serious consideration of the design hypothesis and argued its scientific credentials, Behe defined irreducible complexity to describe systems such as vision and molecular machines that depend on a large number of interrelated parts. "By *irreducibly complex*," he says, "I mean a single system composed of several well-matched, interacting parts that contribute to the basic function, wherein the removal of any one of the parts causes the system to effectively cease functioning." Dr Phillip Johnson put the idea this way: "Each biochemical system requires a stupefyingly complex set of components which affect each other in intricate ways. No component makes sense except as part of the system, and the system doesn't work unless everything is in place. That's irreducible complexity."[8]

Let's recap some of the features of human eyes, *all of which work together* to produce vision:

- A skull structure with eye sockets to accommodate the eye parts and muscles
- An opening through the skull for the nerves to pass to the brain
- A brain structure with neurons configured to accept electrical impulses from the nerves and to form a visual image—in stereo
- Memory to store the images (how many terabytes?)
- A properly shaped eyeball with the right fluid interior
- A transparent surface (cornea) of the right shape to help focus light
- A flexible, transparent lens with variable index of refraction, with muscles to adjust the focal length and nerves to provide feedback
- An iris around the lens with muscles to open and close it to compensate for brightness of the light; plus, a brain that knows how to operate the muscles automatically, with feedback from the eye
- Waveguides to aim the light at the receptors
- A retina of rods and cones located precisely at the focal plane of the lens to capture the image
- Enzymes in the rods and cones to respond to the light, then transmit electrical impulses to the optic nerve

- Blood vessels to supply nutrients to the eye, muscles, tear glands, nerves, and retina and carry off waste products
- A clear gelatinous substance in the eyeball to maintain shape and pass light unimpeded from the lens to the rods and cones
- A series of four muscles to move the eyeball up, down, and sideways, controlled by nerves from the brain
- Tissues in the eye socket to lubricate and protect the eyeball and muscles
- Tear ducts at the edge of the eye capable of producing a fluid of just the right chemical composition to clean and lubricate the cornea
- Flexible eyelids of skin to protect the eyeball and distribute the tear fluid
- Muscles to operate the eyelids, controlled by nerves from the right spot in the brain, able to be operated intentionally or automatically
- All of these parts in pairs, working in tandem to produce stereoscopic images

Each feature is part of a unified whole. We intuitively know that they constitute a system for the purpose of seeing. Unguided natural processes know nothing of systems arranged for a function. If any of these items in the 'parts list' emerged by accident, would natural selection somehow 'know' to keep it for future use? No. Unguided processes have no foresight. To function together as a system, all the parts have to be present in the same individual at the same time.

Keep this concept in mind as we continue to showcase examples of such integrated systems in this book—not just vision, but other parts of the human body and of animals large and small, familiar and unfamiliar. These are brute facts of nature that deserve worthy scientific explanations—rational theories enjoining necessary and sufficient causes that can account for their astonishing features, here on this amazing Spacecraft Earth.

The X-rated part

To me, one of the most exquisite aspects of the human body is the portion directed to reproduction. The whole process that results in the birth of a new human being is such a phenomenal design that there is really no way to improve on it. The union of sperm and egg is obviously essential to the continuation of any sexual species, and in humans, the equipment to accomplish it is wondrous. The sexual equipment in both genders is so perfectly matched on so many levels that trying to imagine any way they came about through chance mistakes strains credibility.

Sex involves much more than just having perfectly fitting sex organs. It entails complexity on multiple levels, from psychology to the proteins in the gametes. We are learning that a sperm cell, for instance, carries with it proteins essential to the development of the embryo. The egg, in addition, contains proteins that allow one (and only one) sperm cell to break through the exterior membrane, then immediately blocks others. The internal organs that develop ovum and sperm (each undergoing specialized cell divisions that result in half the normal complement of paired chromosomes) is another level of staggering complexity. Then, there have to be systems of storing and delivering the gametes, implanting the zygote, and preparing the female for nourishing it. All those glands and organs, in turn, require blood vessels and nerves. Recent 'movies' of how an unborn baby develops in the womb rightly arouse awe and wonder at the whole choreographed process. After the miracle of birth, the continuing development from baby to child, through puberty and on to adult is beautiful to behold.

The innate sex drive or urge, which draws the male and female together, is certainly a crucial ingredient. If that sex urge was slowly developed over evolutionary eons, how did reproduction take place from a starting point of no urge, to the development of an urge? Try to imagine a species with only sex organs or only a sex urge; it would quickly go extinct. The sex drive (which is both a physical and psychological activity) had to be operative simultaneously with the arrival of the sex organs.

Human sex organs are significantly different from those of other animals, particularly monkeys. As with so many other human features (such as the bones in the human foot), the human form is much more than an upgrade; it's more like a remake. At the risk of getting too graphic, the human female has one gland that no other animal has, called the clitoris. Unlike most other body parts, it seems to have only one purpose and that is to give the human female sexual pleasure and stimulation. How in the midst of developing all that is in this chapter, did undirected evolution produce this body part? How indeed?

No other mammal makes love face to face. No other mammal engages the whole body in the embrace. No other primate experiences sex at such a deep emotional, psychological and spiritual level. We create songs, poetry, novels, ballets and opera about love. We blush and experience shame when love crosses moral boundaries. We are outraged when it is forced. We rejoice when it is holy and pure. No other primate has such a long maturation period, with so long a time for the father and mother to teach and train the young in good behavior, for the welfare of the society. This is no upgrade. It shows a very elegant level of design, not only for the good of the individual or species, but for the good of the planet.

The brain: the ultimate operating system

The human brain has been called the most complex piece of organized matter in the entire universe. One human brain has more computing power and data storage capacity than all the computers and memory storage devices that are in existence! Yet this works in a space only 1700 cubic centimeters in volume, weighing just three pounds. Almost all animals have a brain of sorts, but the human brain is orders of magnitude more sophisticated in both structure and function. With its 100 billion neurons, each making up to thousands of connections with neighboring neurons, the human brain has more connections than all the appliances in the world combined.

The brain undergoes refining and changes during the maturation of a person. A couple of months before birth, the brain will have grown the maximum number of cells it will have for its lifetime. Over the next couple dozen years, the brain develops patterns and cell connections, and discards many cells that have not turned out to be essential. So if you can imagine that small brain in a developed embryo, it has generated these billions of neurons in just a few months. What kind of foreman could build something that sophisticated that fast? As a foreman, DNA is unsurpassed. A growing fetus must be an absolute frenzy of activity as all the organs, tissue, bones, muscles, nerves, and, of course, the brain builds and develops. And then at birth, everything switches on, and just works. The lungs are ready to use air, the stomach to receive and digest food. The salivary glands start working. The swallowing reflex works. The voice works. Everything just works!

The structure of brain cells is immensely detailed down to the molecular level. Neurons are self-programming and adapt as we learn and remember stimuli. They do not always retain every memory perfectly (as some of us who are getting long in the tooth find out), but if we do use our brains actively, they can contain almost limitless numbers of details with time tags.

I want to show you a rendition of one set of such interconnecting cells from an article in *Chemical & Engineering News*. This is an article well worth looking up. It states:

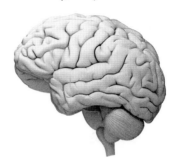

Bigstock

Figure 2-14. Gray matter
More computing power than all man-made machines put together

Anatomists and physiologists have been uncovering some of these [brain operation] mechanisms for more than a century. With its 100 billion or so neurons—each one a living electrochemical wonder that connects via cell-to-cell synapses with then, hundreds, or sometimes many thousands of other neurons—the brain's cellular architecture itself offers a gargantuan number of possible states for storing and processing information.

A recent calculation by Danish neuroscientists suggests that the human brain's neocortex alone harbors approximately 150 million synapses. Add to that architectural complexity the ability of neurons to rewire their synaptic liaisons, tweak their chemical microenvironments, and change their firing patterns, and the number of possible brain states skyrockets.[9]

The brain controls everything in the body, sending its commands down thousands of nerve fibers, each of which originates somewhere in the brain. Then each nerve cell terminates in some muscle or sensor to fulfill the brain's direction, and sends back information on its status. The nerves all funnel down the inside of the protective spine, and split out all along the way to reach their points of action. It all fits together perfectly, according to a design that no human could replicate. It's all there at the right place, at the right time, with the right function. It's unimaginable that something like that could come about by a series of chance mistakes.

Let's look at this in a little more detail. The postcranial central nervous system contains some 11 billion nerve cells connected in elaborate networks, but they don't all do the same job. Some nerves bring sensory signals to the brain giving us a sense of touch, heat, light, sound, smell, or taste. Other nerves are command carriers operating muscles; some of these nerves are very long single cells, some running the length of the body. Each nerve starts or terminates at a specific place in the brain to process the sensory inputs at command centers that either monitor the body's vast systems, or initiate actions of the muscles. Most nerve cells have a long extension, called an axon, plus a number of dendrites that interact with other nerve cells. As a baby develops in the womb, all those billions of neurons reach out and make the right connections at the right time, so that at birth, all systems are 'go' for life. Does this sound like the work of random mistakes and aimless processes of natural selection? Eons of time are not going to help get a job like this done.

Inside the brain and throughout the body, nerve cells transmit signals through a combination of electrical impulses and chemical exchanges between nerve endings (see Figure 2-15). The amount of signaling going on, even during sleep, is staggering. From every part of the exterior skin, to every organ inside, to the beehive of constant activity in the brain, the body is abuzz with signals. Just like

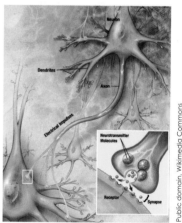

Figure 2-15. **Synapses**
Interconnections of human brain cells

a highway system, the 'rural roads' of nerve pathways converge into the superhighways of the central nervous system, up the protective spine into the brain and down again with new signals.

There are two main nerve systems: the central nervous system, and the peripheral nervous system. The central nervous system communicates with every organ, and knows with uncanny accuracy how to route the signals from the right starting to the right end point. Think how all 100 billion neurons grew in the human embryo in just a few months' time. Each nerve cell had to start somewhere and grow its axon down the spinal cord, leave the spine at the right place through the right opening, and then connect up at the designated location. One hundred billion of them! Somehow the DNA directs the growth in a deterministic way, according to a plan that is basically the same in every human body. This allows us to not only live independently, with our minds, arms, legs and organs all working, but to relate to other human beings on a deep neurological level. If we saw a robotic factory accomplishing one hundred-thousandth of this kind of accurate work, we would not hesitate for a moment to conclude it was intelligently designed.

As I said earlier, the thing about which I marvel most is the human body. We looked at it briefly in this chapter. It is the subject that started me on the path to writing this book. When we look at the gap between our supposed nearest ancestor, the chimpanzee, we see an almost infinite number of improvements that have made us rulers of the world and conquerors of space while our supposed ancestors are left swinging in the trees. Can you imagine the billions of lucky mutations that would have had to take place—in both males and females—to arrive at beings capable of language, upright posture, civilization, music, and abstract thought? One is compelled to ask: how could it happen?

It does not take much knowledge of biology or physiology to develop a long list of human characteristics to illustrate this point. Consider the capability of the human brain, which is almost limitless, versus the brain of an ape screeching from the treetops. The human ability to reason, to imagine, to calculate, to have emotions, to make music, to control bodily functions by force of will, is almost infinitely superior to that possessed by chimpanzees. How could all of these powers have 'emerged' by mistake in the limited time span (about 7 million years) allowed by evolutionists? The age of the universe would not suffice for that amount of luck.

The diversity between humans is also interesting. You see one chimpanzee, you've pretty much seen them all. Human beings, though, are remarkable for their differences. We're all one human race, but each human face is unique and recognizable. We differ not only in height and skin color and other physical characteristics, but in our mental and emotional proclivities as well. Some people have artistic abilities, some mechanical abilities, some mathematical abilities. Some are scientifically curious, while others excel at empathy. This diversity works out in civilization, where everyone can contribute their own skills and talents for the good of all. How did natural selection produce that?

Human distinctives

The wonders of the human body could occupy volumes. How about the fact that we have nerves on the outer surface of the body that give us the sense of touch, temperature, pain, and even pleasure, but have very few of the same kind inside the body? If all the internal organs had a sense of touch, what turmoil we would face daily! Oh, my liver is rubbing against my stomach again, I wonder why? Oh, my diaphragm is pressuring my right lung, what does that mean? We do have internal nerves as they are needed; for instance, we feel an empty or full stomach, a stomachache, being out of breath, a full bladder, and other important indicators. But we have just what we need—no less, no more—to carry on our lives without consciously thinking about each internal organ all the time.

Consider also the symmetry of the body: we have left and right sides, with backups for kidneys and lungs, eyes and limbs, but we only have one liver, one heart, and one digestive tract. How does the developing embryo know which items to duplicate, and where to put them? How does it know to put the left kidney on the left side, and the right kidney on the right side? Why are not some people born with two left feet, if mistakes are the way evolution makes progress? Mistakes do occur, but they usually kill an organism or leave it less fit, not more fit. The question we should ask is not why mistakes occur, but why they are so rare. Dr Joseph L. Henson used to say in his biology classes at Bob Jones University, "The amazing thing is not that we get sick, but that we are ever well."[10] Given the number of places where things could go wrong, it's amazing most of us do live quite well into old age, our hearts beating reliably for decades, our digestive tracts usually managing to deal with the stuff we gulp down.

We've looked at just a few wonders in the human body: the foot, the elbow, saliva, milk, the brain, the eye, and some others, but with these, we barely have begun. The human body shouts "Design!" Evolution could not handle the number of 'mistakes' that would be

3

The Other Passengers: Plants and Animals

The match of organisms to their environments on Spacecraft Earth is striking: fish to swimming, birds to flying, and plants to collecting and processing sunlight—these are but individual jewels in a vast treasure chest of life. We will look at a few gems in this chapter, but first, let's discuss efficiency and optimality.

Design perfection

Studies of bird and bat flight, dolphin sonar, sea turtle navigation and a host of other organisms have led to the conclusion by some scientists that many creatures have achieved engineering 'nirvana' of sorts: optimal design. Somehow, animals and plants arrived at the best designs possible, given the environmental constraints and trade-offs involved. This means that it would be virtually impossible to improve on the design. We've seen this in the case of the human eye, where waveguides provide one-to-one correspondence between photon and receptor. We'll see it later in molecular machines like ATP synthase and the bacterial flagellum, both operating at essentially 100% efficiency—achievements thought impossible in engineering. And after decades of research trying to study photosynthesis in plants, biochemists have found that the light receptors in chloroplasts act like quantum antennas, able to capture individual photons of light—

yet the chloroplasts also employ 'quenching' mechanisms to avoid overheating in bright light. Engineering doesn't get better than this.

'Optimal design' is increasingly being reported in large-scale systems in the plant and animal kingdoms as well. For instance, the spacing of gills in fish has been found to be optimal for oxygen absorption. In bats' wings, tiny hair-thin muscles keep the membranes taut for maximum flexibility during maneuvers in the air. A female wasp has an egg-laying tool called an ovipositor that is 'immensely long' for its size, yet thinner than a human hair, but able to cut through the woody rind of an unripe fig with its serrated edges tipped with zinc. Ants have a search strategy that solves a well-known optimization puzzle called the 'Chinese postman problem'—how to find the most efficient route between multiple points. And birds have collision-avoidance systems that allow 500,000 starlings to fly in formation without crashing into each other—something fighter pilots can only dream of.

Flight systems

Consider the wings and feathers of a bird. Feathers are marvels of design all the way down to the microscopic scale. Lightweight, waterproof and flexible, flight feathers have a hook-and-ridge microstructure that is strong but not heavy. They allow some bird species to spend almost their entire lives on the wing. Common swifts

Figure 3-1. **Parts of a flight feather**

have been measured spending up to ten months at a time in the air without landing.[1]

Growing feathers on a dinosaur will not allow it take off into the air. Every system on a flying animal must work in concert to meet the stringent demands of flight. In birds, the center of gravity is compact, with the muscles located below the wings. The digestive system is designed for maximum efficiency. The bones are hollow with girders and struts for maximum durability with minimum weight. The unique avian lung allows one-way passage of air. The shape of the wings, legs, and tail are fine-tuned for flight.

As a class, most birds possess these traits in common. If we look within the class Aves (birds), we find additional specialized matches: hummingbirds that can hover in midair due to unique shoulder bones that rotate up to 140 degrees; Arctic terns that can fly from pole to pole and return unerringly to the exact island they started from; starlings that can fly in formation in groups of half a million birds, diving birds whose eyes instantly adjust at the air-water interface to see underwater; flightless birds like ostriches that can outrun a horse. Penguins are the only birds without hollow bones, because they need denser bones for swimming.[2]

Specializations within categories

Similar observations about category traits and specializations can be made about any group one chooses. Take any group of plants or animals, living or extinct, and you will find exquisite examples of adaptation to the environment, both general and specific. Fish are ideal swimmers in general, but within the fish category are species with unique matches: halibut that can rotate eyes onto the backs of their heads, flying fish that can glide in the air, deep-sea fish that can attract prey in the dark with glowing lures. The colorations and patterns in fish seem unlimited, even though all fish share the same basic body plan.

Within Mammalia, we find elephants with long flexible trunks, beavers able to gnaw down trees and build dams, and gibbons swinging through trees more nimbly than circus acrobats. Within cephalopods we find octopuses that can imitate other sea creatures and disappear from view on a rock, giant squid that can fight whales, and cuttlefish that can generate fast-changing color-and-pattern displays on their skin. Among insects, we find dragonflies that can mate while hovering in mid-air and process 'optic flow' information using specialized visual organs called ocelli, honeybees that build hexagonal hives and share information about food distance and angle to the sun via dances; and ants that have basically taken over the world—even affecting its geology and climate.[3]

Evolutionists would have us believe that all these matches to the environment are the product of unguided natural processes. No intelligence was involved, they say; they just 'look' designed for a purpose. It may have taken a rare sequence of mutations to get to the end product, but the fit of organism to environment is what remained after all the ne'er-do-wells lost out and went extinct. If that were true, though, we would still have cause to be astonished to see so many end products—the wing of a bird, the eye of a mammal—achieve near perfection via unguided processes. It might even seem miraculous.

Honeybees and flowers

Plants need honeybees to effectively perform pollination. Honeybees use the pollen for food and also to produce honey. Did bees and flowers develop independently, and then, by chance, develop a synergistic relationship between them that is now necessary for both?

Self-pollination in a plant does happen without insects' help, but it is a very inefficient process. It depends largely on external disturbances, like wind, to dislodge pollen from the male organ (the stamen) and somehow conduct it to the female organ (the pistil). If flowers had to depend on self-pollination, they would become very scarce because reproduction and the generation of seeds would be inefficient, and the number of new plants would be quite few. But without pollen from flowers, many insects would have nothing to eat.

Figure 3-2. **Honeycomb**
Hexagonal grid of wax cells built by humble honeybees

Honeybees are more than just efficient pollinators. They build hives of geometrical perfection, and form societies with multiple cooperative roles. Their hives, like those of termites, are air-conditioned so that the larvae can incubate effectively. When it gets too hot, specialized workers will fan the interior with their wings. Most remarkable of all, honeybees communicate with an elaborate 'waggle dance' language that tells their hive mates the direction to a food source with respect to the angle of the sun, the distance, and the quality of the food. This allows the other bees to carry just enough food to reach the source—not too much, to weigh them down, or too little, such that they run out of fuel before arriving.

Recent studies have shown that honeybees also take advantage of polarized light for information sharing. They do all these actions with tiny brains that are marvels of microengineering. With 950,000 neurons packed into the space of a pinhead, honeybee brains have stunned biologists with their conceptual abilities that rival those of primates.

The bee's nourishment comes entirely from pollen produced by flowering plants. The plants need the bees to move the pollen from stamen to pistil. Insects and plants are separated by a vast genetic distance, according to evolutionary theory. How did blind processes of evolution create this tight symbiotic arrangement? It's just one of many remarkable interactions in nature called 'mutualistic symbioses', where totally different creatures are well adapted to work together for their common benefit.

The mantis shrimp

This colorful crustacean has caught the attention of marine biologists for its incredible capabilities. The mantis shrimp is the only animal known with eyes able to detect circularly polarized light. This creature can see better than humans can! It has 16 color sensors compared to our three, and is able to see into the ultraviolet range. Its eyes come coated with a specialized sunscreen that also serves as a spectral filter.

That would be enough to attract attention, but the mantis shrimp wins another gold medal in the animal Olympics: it has the toughest hammer in the animal kingdom. Its claw strikes so fast

Public domain, Wikimedia Commons

Figure 3-3. **Mantis shrimp**

(accelerating at 10,000 g's), it can break the glass in an aquarium with one blow! Scientists are eager to learn how the claw can hit so fast and so hard—delivering a force a thousand times the animal's weight—and do it over and over again a thousand times between molts. *Science* magazine called it "a formidable damage-tolerant biological hammer".[4]

The mantis shrimp appears 'overdesigned' for mere survival. It could certainly get by with less, like many other sea creatures do, if its only goal in life was to survive and reproduce. A car need not be a Ferrari to drive down the road. How can evolutionary theory account for such extraordinary capabilities? Yet examples of 'gratuitous design' can be multiplied as we look at the living world.

Diatoms

About 20% of the oxygen we breathe is produced by little one-celled algae called diatoms. Though too small to be seen without a microscope (five to ten of them could fit on the head of a pin), they are some of the most beautiful creatures on earth. The 100,000 some-odd species of diatoms come in a variety of geometric shapes—circles, rods, triangles, stars, and more elaborate shapes—and are decorated with intricate patterns front and back.

Diatoms live in glass houses they create from silica dissolved in fresh or salt water. The shells, called 'tests', fit together like halves of a pill box. The patterns on the tests are so detailed, microscope manufacturers used them for years to test the quality of their optics. How can such tiny creatures create these artworks from material dissolved in seawater? How does a blind one-celled creature know how to construct a five-pointed star?

Diatoms are among the most abundant creatures on the planet. One diatom expert called them "the most important little

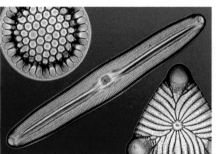

Composite image / Anatoly Mikhaltsov / Wikimedia Commons, CC BY-SA 4.0

Figure 3-4. Diatoms
Algae that build microscopic glass houses

organisms that most people have never heard of." They "play an immense role in keeping the planet's ecosystem working," he said, noting that in addition to providing oxygen, they are the principal cyclers of silica that makes up about a fourth of the earth's crust.[5] The White Cliffs of Dover and some other huge geological formations are made up almost entirely of diatom remains. We depend on diatoms, but we weren't able to appreciate their beauty until the invention of the microscope. It's as if the Creator kept some secrets in his treasure chest for later generations to discover.

Seed dispersal

Plants have many ingenious methods of dispersing their seeds; we can only mention a few examples here. Cockleburs adhere to clothing and cattle fur (this was the inspiration for Velcro). Coconuts and mangrove pods can float across the ocean to colonize distant shores. Some seeds resist digestion, traveling through the digestive tracts of birds or mammals as they are carried far from their starting point. And some seeds are launched like cannonballs through the air by pressurized pods. The pods of the Scotchbroom, for instance, are designed to create extreme tension as they dry out. The slightest touch can make them explode, launching their seeds as far as 50 feet.

Figure 3-5. **Long distance travelers**
Dandelion seeds

Some of the most interesting seeds are those carried by wind. Who does not chuckle at the ingenuity of the tumbleweed, whose seeds mature just as the main stem weakens and breaks? The plant becomes a highly efficient seed sowing machine. Dandelion seeds—the delight of many children—can drift on breezes for miles. Maple seeds, called samaras, act like perfect little helicopter blades that can be carried far from the tree in an updraft; their design has attracted the attention of aeronautical engineers.

But surpassing even these in ingenuity are the drillers and crawlers that only reveal their ways in time-lapse movies. An insignificant plant in California called the filaree folds its rapidly-opening seed pod into a drill that can actually power itself into the soil. And the filaments on wild oats turn into biological motors when they drop to the ground. Though separated from the plant, their work just begins. Alternating wet and dry cycles from day to night cause the filaments to twist clockwise and counterclockwise, becoming motorized propellers for the attached seeds. In time-lapse, the seeds look like little robots or bugs scurrying across the landscape. They can even dive into the soil, planting themselves without any farmer's help.

Archer fish

There's a small freshwater fish in India that can spit bugs off the limbs of overhead plants. This 'archer fish' has attracted the attention of physicists, because the fish has to overcome several problems of physics to be able to do this.[6] As the fish looks up from underwater at a target bug, it has to correct for the change in index of refraction between water and air. It has to be able to reliably estimate the distance. Then, it has to deliver the right amount of force from

Figure 3-6. **Archer fish**

its mouth to dislodge the bug, which is probably clinging tightly to the branch. Yet the archer fish rarely misses, even up to a height of ten feet.

Further research has shown that the fish actually fine-tunes its jets for extra punch. Slow-motion video has shown that the fish emits a series of spits, with the later ones traveling faster. The jets converge into a watery cannonball, delivering a mega-wallop that is much more powerful than a single jet would be. How did this little fish learn physics? One biologist observing this wondered if the fish was developing cognitive abilities like humans, under the evolutionary notion that throwing spears led our species to evolve bigger brains.

Hummingbird tongue

Most everyone loves watching hummingbirds, with their colorful feathers, hovering in mid-air and even flying backward as they zip from flower to flower for nectar. Their shoulder bones and wings are specially adapted for these motions, allowing the wings (unlike those of any other bird) to rotate and achieve lift on both forward and backward strokes. The hummingbird's high metabolic

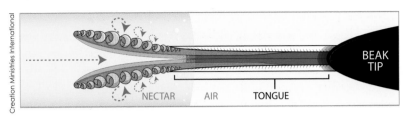

Creation Ministries International

Figure 3-7. Hummingbird tongue
Unfurling flaps gather up nectar on a forked tongue.

rate requires a very rapid heartbeat to keep those wings flapping at up to 70 times per second.

Another surprising design was only discovered recently. It involves the method the hummingbird uses to draw nectar into its mouth. The tongue is not just a straw-like organ pulling up nectar by capillary action; it's actually a well-designed nectar trap. When the tongue reaches deep into a flower and enters a pool of nectar, the tongue splits into two strands. Each strand is equipped with tiny flaps attached to a supporting rod. The flaps automatically unfurl in the liquid. As the tongue is withdrawn, each flap wraps around the liquid and seals it tightly, creating two tubes full of nectar that are then drawn into the mouth.[6]

Another clever aspect of the design came to light even more recently. The hummingbird flattens its tongue as it exits the tip of the beak. It stays flat until it contacts the nectar, then it expands. This literally 'pumps' the nectar into the tongue, filling it quickly. Then, the flaps seal it in to deliver a full load into the bird's mouth.[7]

This action requires no muscles; it's all automatic. And it takes place in less than 1/20th of second, thousands of times a day. It would be hard to imagine a man-made device this delicate that could perform so consistently every day for years.

Perching birds

Birds' feet share a common pattern, but each type of bird has special adaptations for its own needs. Chickens, for example, spend much time scratching on the ground, while woodpeckers cling tightly to trunks of trees. Ornithologists (biologists who study birds) have found important differences in the toe arrangements and the tendons that control them.

Perching birds, such as the chicken and the canary, have three toes forward and one toe back. They have only one tendon that controls all four toes. When the bird lands on a branch and bends its knee, the tendon automatically pulls over the knee, clamping the toes around the branch with a vise-like grip—a great benefit when the bird needs to sleep in the tree. The toes only release when the bird straightens its leg.

Climbers and creepers, such as parakeets and woodpeckers, have two toes pointing forward and two pointing back. They have two tendons, one for the front pair, one for the back pair, perfect for supporting their weight on tree trunks. But birds of prey—owls, hawks and eagles—have talons pointing in four directions, with a separate tendon for each talon. This allows them to clutch and manipulate their prey. Once again, while we see groups of animals sharing general traits, each species comes equipped with just the right form of those traits for its particular needs.

Electric eels

It has been said that the electric eel of the Amazon can 'light up a neon sign, kill a horse at 20 feet, and distinguish friend from foe at 40 feet.' How can a biological organism made of watery tissues generate electricity? The instruments I worked on for JPL used metal and had to be kept dry. We may have liquid-based batteries in our cars, but we don't typically try to operate them underwater!

Lt. Col. Lyell M. Rader described how fish generate electricity in a 1998 book, *Romance and Dynamite*:

> The generating mechanism for such voltage is located in three columns running the length of its body. These columns are voltaic piles composed of alternate conductive and dielectric, or insulating, tissue. Each column in a large eel can generate 300 volts at ten amperes. These columns are wired in series (negative to positive). Wired in this manner, the combined kick is 900 volts at ten amperes, the perfect killing current for fresh water.
>
> The electric ray of the salt water ocean is very different in appearance, but has virtually the same equipment. There are three columns producing 300 volts each at ten amperes, but the columns are wired parallel instead of in series (negatives

wired together, and positives wired together). Wired in this manner, the kick remains at 300 volts, but at three times the current, 30 amperes. This is the perfect killing current for salt water.[8]

Rader asked how a creature could not only arrive at this electrical genius by trial and error, but also control the switching, which is quite different in the two species. "There are no pitted switch points or burned contacts in either creature," he noted; the creatures are designed with the right 'solid state physics' to generate electricity underwater, store it, and release it on command.

How could such a marvel come about? Rader points out four design requirements:

> Granted, some creatures do look unbelievably odd, but they all have one thing in common: they work. This requires four simultaneous endowments: first, complex apparatus; second, instinctive know-how to operate the equipment; third, motivation to operate the equipment at the right moment; and fourth, in an environment where it perfectly fits into the balance of nature by just the right ratio of advantage to disadvantage, birthrate to death rate.[9]

It would be astonishing enough if these requirements had been met by trial and error in one species. But now, consider that electricity generation or electrical sensing equipment is found in multiple unrelated organisms: the electric eels (bony fish), electric rays (cartilaginous fish), and even the platypus (a mammal). Evolutionists teach, in all seriousness, that this ability arose independently six times in fish alone! They call this 'convergent evolution', but it appears more like a hand-waving escape from explanation than a true scientific attempt at explaining effects by means of rational causes.

Salmon

The sight of salmon leaping waterfalls while escaping the paws of hungry bears is one of those memorable scenes we enjoy on TV nature shows. But it's only a small chapter in a remarkable story. Young salmon, when hatched, are born with a magnetic map that will guide them thousands of miles back to their birthplace years later. They also memorize the smells of their birthplace with 'odor maps' built from a remarkable 'combinatorial code' sent to the brain from their olfactory (smell) organs. As a juvenile salmon swims downstream, slight changes in magnetism (both field intensity and orientation), and changes in odor concentrations are memorized in the brain, creating a route map. It will need this information as an adult.[10]

Adolescent salmon will spend a few days at the mouth of the stream adjusting to salt water. This remarkable process involves several drastic physiological changes. Molecular pumps in the gills reverse direction, pumping salt out of the blood instead of in. The kidneys drastically reduce production of urine, and the fish drinks in more water. The freshwater fish is ready to enter the salty ocean.

The growing salmon will travel for hundreds of miles, sometimes thousands of miles, as it explores the trackless ocean, following invisible currents, knowing instinctively where the best feeding areas are. Years later, the urge to reproduce becomes strong. How will the fish get back? Birds and butterflies can use the sun or stars as guides, but much of the ocean is featureless. The salmon's unerring sense of direction comes from its exquisite magnetic sense. Tiny flecks of magnetite in the brain orient to the earth's magnetic field. The fish uses that compass needle with its stored 'magnetic map' to find the way back to the home stream.

As it nears the mouth of the stream, the salmon's challenges are just beginning. Once again, it must reverse its physiology to acclimate to fresh water. Then, it will go 'against the flow' of strong currents and powerful water-

Figure 3-8. **Excellent navigators**
Salmon use the earth's magnetic field to help them migrate from the ocean back to their native stream.

Illustra Media / Living Waters film

falls, leaping with all its muscular might toward the scent of home. Many will fall prey to hungry bears and other predators along the way. The call of that birthplace is overpowering, and the salmon's navigational equipment is up to the task of finding it. Its olfactory organs are precise enough to distinguish parts-per-billion changes in odors between tributary streams.

Once again home, after having been away for years, the fish spawn. Their work done, their energy spent, they coast downstream and die. A new generation of hatchlings, born with the magnetic map and the instincts it will need, repeats this amazing cycle of life.

These are but glimpses of a multifaceted 'system of systems', all coordinated, each one with better specifications than we used in the space program. Most fish have a 'lateral line' along their flanks, for instance, that acts as a finely tuned sensory organ for identifying currents and electrical properties of the water. Fish muscles are arranged in W-shaped sheets called myomeres running front to back (these are visible in store-bought salmon), which give them their flexibility for swimming. We haven't even begun to talk about eyes, ears, nervous systems, digestive systems, and all the other systems salmon share with vertebrates.

Could these systems evolve by unguided natural processes? Without all of them working in coordination, no offspring would result. Not all salmon migrate, and those that do can adjust for changing environments, but the equipment involved is very precise. Experiments have shown, for instance, that salmon will orient to magnetic fields too weak to deflect a compass needle. Each odor molecule fits like a lock and key to the odor receptors in the nasal passages. The physiological equipment to adjust from fresh water to salt water and back is irreducibly complex; without each part, the fish would die. Everything the salmon needs for every stage is present, in good working order, from birth to death.

Metamorphosis

All insects go through dramatic changes during their life stages between egg, maggot, pupa and adult, but none are as spectacular as those of butterflies and moths. Consider the difference between a caterpillar and a butterfly. A caterpillar can only crawl; a butterfly takes to the air on gossamer wings. A caterpillar eats leaves; a butterfly drinks nectar. Caterpillars lack sex organs; butterflies reproduce with eggs and sperm. The eyes and legs of caterpillars are completely different from the articulated limbs, wings, and compound eyes of the adult. Mature butterflies, also, have antennae with extremely sensitive organs of smell, able to detect faint pheromones from a mile away.

Most wondrous of all butterflies—indeed, in the entire animal kingdom—are the migrating species. The Monarch butterflies of North America travel up to 3,000 miles each year from Canada to Mexico. Every fourth generation or so, eggs hatch with a special ability to survive for six months instead of the usual 6 to 8 weeks. This 'Methuselah generation' flies almost nonstop to the exact same trees where its great-grand-parents wintered the prior year, never having flown that route before. How do they do it? Scientists are not sure, but know that they can navigate by the earth's magnetic field, the sun's position, and perhaps the stars. Recently, the Monarchs were bested by another species: the painted lady butterflies of England. Scientists found that they migrate an astonishing 6,000 miles on their annual journeys.

Pexels.com

Figure 3-9. Monarch butterfly
These insects perform incredible migration feats.

Schoolchildren learn how caterpillars spin a cocoon (for but-terflies, called a chrysalis), out of which an adult emerges some two weeks later. What goes on in that mysterious chamber? Scientists know that most of the tissues of the caterpillar break down into a nearly shapeless liquid. Certain controlling organs, called imaginal disks, direct the formation of antennae, mouth parts, legs, wings, sex organs, and all the other things the adult will need for its aerial life, out of those recycled parts. MRI and CT scans have revealed the elaborate production process at work in more detail than ever before, but many details remain mysterious. One thing is sure: when the adult hatches out, within minutes it is completely operational, flying and using all that new equipment. A documentary film about this likened it to a Model-T building a garage around itself, tearing its parts down, and re-assembling them into a helicopter.[11] That may be understating the case. It's a complete redesign!

Think of what a challenge this is to evolutionary theory. Caterpil-lars cannot reproduce. When the caterpillar enters the chrysalis, it's basically entering its own casket. Unless its genes can keep that distant goal of a butterfly in mind, and follow all the procedures correctly, the creature will die. Nothing further will evolve by natural selection. Think of how many coordinated mutations had to get the process just right so that the adult butterfly would not only emerge from the chrysalis, but have working wings and sex organs to carry on the species for the next generation. And how does the Methuselah generation emerge on cue after three normal generations, with extra longevity and strength to fly 3,000 miles, knowing where to go? Believing that a blind, unguided process got all of this right is equivalent to believing in multiple miracles.

Figure 3-10. **Monarch chrysalis**

The bombardier beetle

One of my favorite examples of a creature that defies evolution is a bug that fires hot explosives at its enemies. The bombardier beetle challenges evolution because the bug would blow itself up if it didn't get it right! This amazing insect uses two separate chambers in its abdomen, one for the explosive (hydrogen peroxide) and one for the detonator (hydroquinone). These chemicals must be kept separate and in a deactivated state. When they are mixed in the combustion chamber, they must be activated at just the right time, in the right amounts, and in the right way, or else the bug will be a victim of its own weapon, unable to reproduce.

How could such a system evolve? Everything had to work right from the beginning, or no offspring would see the light of day to pass along the lucky discovery. Rader explains,

> All of these systems have to be in flawless working conditions for the beetle to survive. The cannons without the explosives would be meaningless. One chemical without the other would not explode. Both chemicals, without the inhibitor, would blow the beetle to bits. Without the anti-inhibitor, the beetle would be unable to trigger the explosion at all. Without the storage chambers, it wouldn't have the chemicals on hand when needed. Without strongly reinforced, heat-proof combustion tubes and cannons, the heat generated by the explosion would cook the beetle.

But most amazing of all is the hair trigger communications system. The beetle identifies a potential enemy; waits until the enemy gets its mouth open; pulls the anti-inhibitor like a firing pin on a rifle; aims its cannons; and sends a scalding blast of noxious gas from its tail into the mouth of the aggressor, curbing its appetite for any more beetles. These five functions must be perfectly timed to a fraction of a second.[12]

Figure 3-11.
Bombardier beetle

There's more to this story. High speed cameras have shown that the beetle fires a rapid series of shots rather than one explosive burst. This gives the bug finer control over the explosion, preventing the recoil that would send it flying. The beetle can also aim its heat weapon precisely over a wide range of angles. All these controls require additional 'brain software' for their use.

Is it any wonder that creationists have enjoyed pointing to the bombardier beetle as a challenge to evolution? We are aware that evolutionists are clever at comeback arguments; they can tell stories after the fact, imagining how a series of mutations might have been naturally selected over millions of years to produce such things. What we should notice is that imagined stories are necessary in their view. Irreducibly complex systems like the bombardier beetle should not be expected in an evolutionary world of happenstance.

Atheist Richard Dawkins famously said, "Biology is the study of complicated things that give the appearance of having been designed for a purpose."[13] Everyone agrees, in other words, that things *look* designed. To deny design, the evolutionist has to choose against the obvious. That's why Francis Crick told his fellow evolutionists, "Biologists must constantly keep in mind that what they see was not designed, but rather evolved."[14]

Practical design

The ubiquity of optimal designs in life has given rise to a lively and growing branch of science known as *Biomimetics*—the imitation of nature's designs. Why design something from scratch, when nature shows us the best possible solution to many problems we face? We can only share a few examples from this emerging field, but biomimetics is a very active research program now. Whole university departments have sprung up recently to pursue 'Biomimicry' resulting from 'Bio-inspiration' at nature's outstanding achievements. These departments are receiving millions of dollars in government grants, often from the military. Here are just a few examples.

- An engineer invented an all-purpose atomizer fashioned after the bombardier beetle.

- Solar panel designers are trying to mimic photosynthesis.

- The navy is funding efforts to make better submarines inspired by fish.

- Materials scientists are trying to imitate spider silk, an 'ideal material' that is both stretchy and strong, ounce-for-ounce stronger than steel and more flexible than Kevlar.

- Ceramics manufacturers are looking at oysters and teeth to learn how to make self-healing materials that can survive cracking.

- Robot designers are imitating ants, termites and cockroaches for their ability to navigate uneven terrain and communicate in groups.

- Inventors have created a miniature drone that can hover like a hummingbird.

- Car manufacturers would like to make windshields with the 'super-hydrophobic' properties of a lotus leaf. No windshield wipers needed!

- Optics engineers envy the color-reflecting properties of a moth's wing scales, envisioning applications as diverse as clothing and anti-counterfeiting strategies.

- Engineers are learning how geckos can climb walls and glass, so as to make robots that can do the same.

- Medical device manu-facturers are studying barnacles and mussels to learn how to make bio-degradable glue for surgical implants, while shipbuild-ers would like to mimic the barnacle's adhesives that work underwater.

Figure 3-12. **Stickybot**
Modeled after the gecko's ability to climb smooth vertical surfaces

- Factories would like to build robotic arms mimicking the sensitivity and flexibility of an elephant's trunk.

- Computer scientists are trying to mimic the computational strategies of the human brain.

The list of bio-inspired technologies is as long as it is exciting. It sums up nicely what we have been saying: the living world is a world of design perfection. Biomimetics is a scientific approach that is entirely design-focused. It owes nothing to Darwinian theory. It's inspiring a new generation of young scientists. It promotes deeper understanding of biology. And it leads to practical applications that can improve our lives. This is the beauty of design-focused science.

Paul Nelson, a philosopher of biology, recalls something his father taught him: "If something works, it's not happening by accident."[15] Biology works. It works really, really well.

That's a quick look at some non-human marvels in the biology of Spacecraft Earth. Such technology cries out for an explanation. In the next chapter, we will critique some of the most common theories of scientists today.

Public domain, Wikimedia Commons

Figure 3-13.
Robo-trunk

ENDNOTES

1. For 10 months out of the year, common swifts live in mid-air, Science Daily, 27 Oct 2016, sciencedaily.com/releases/2016/10/161027123227.htm.

2. For information on hummingbirds, Arctic terns and starlings, see Illustra Media documentary *Flight: The Genius of Birds* (2012), flightthegeniusofbirds.com.

3. Dorn, R.I., Ants as a powerful biotic agent of olivine and plagioclase dissolution, *Geology* **42**(9):771–774, July 2014, doi: 10.1130/G35825.1.

4. Weaver, J.C., *et al.*, The Stomatopod Dactyl Club: A Formidable Damage-Tolerant Biological Hammer, *Science* **336**(6086):1275–1280, 8 June 2012, science.sciencemag.org/content/336/6086/1275.

5. Alverson, A., The Air You're Breathing? A Diatom Made That, *Live Science,* 10 June 2014, livescience.com/46250-teasing-apart-the-diatom-genome.html.

6. Sarfati, J., Archer fish use advanced hydrodynamics, *Creation* **36**(3):36–37, July 2014, creation.com/archer-fish.

7. Rico-Guevara and Rubega, The hummingbird tongue is a fluid trap, not a capillary tube, *Proceedings of the National Academy of Sciences* **108**(23):9356–9360, 7 June 2011, doi: 10.1073/pnas.1016944108. The action of the tongue is animated in Illustra Media's documentary *Flight: The Genius of Birds*, and can be seen online at: flightthegeniusofbirds.com/clips.php.

8. Rico-Guevara, Fan and Rubega, Hummingbird tongues are elastic micropumps, *Proceedings of the Royal Society B*, 19 Aug 2015, doi: 10.1098/rspb.2015.1014.

9. Rader, L.M., *Romance and Dynamite*, Crest Books, 1998.

10. Rader, *Romance and Dynamite*.

11. The lifestyle of the Pacific salmon is discussed in the Illustra Media documentary *Living Waters: Intelligent Design in the Oceans of the Earth* (2015). Animation of the salmon's sense of smell can be seen at: livingwatersthefilm.com/clips.php.

12. *Metamorphosis: The Beauty and Design of Butterflies,* Illustra Media, 2011. The Model-T animation can be viewed at metamorphosisthefilm.com/clips.php (3rd clip).

13. Rader, *Romance and Dynamite*.

14. Dawkins, R., *The Blind Watchmaker*, W.W. Norton & Company, p.1, 1986.

15. Crick, F., *What Mad Pursuit*, Basic Books, p. 138, 1990.

16. *Flight: The Genius of Birds*.

4

Explaining the Observations

Life presents us with a most astonishing case of both unity and diversity. All of the multitudes of plants and animals, from orchids to sea slugs to giraffes, share a common genetic code with the simplest microbes. Yet that basic coded 'language', written in DNA, generates an incredible variety of creatures and behaviors. With that code, dolphins can identify food with sound, redwoods can pump water almost 400 feet into the sky, and crows can make tools to get food out of tight places. The code directs the development of a chick from an egg in just 21 days. It produced the mighty dinosaurs. It fills the entire biosphere, from deep beneath the ocean to the top of the atmosphere, in every possible niche, with organisms of astonishing complexity. How is this unity and diversity to be explained?

Unity and diversity

It has always fascinated me to observe the closeness of characteristics within a family of organisms, be it animal or plant. How unique are many of them! Yet they all share some characteristics, such as lions and kittens in the cat family. If evolutionary forces required billions of small changes, we would predict a blur or smear of traits blending from one family to another. We would not expect the sharp boundaries between families such as dogs and cats, tomatoes and radishes. This sharp distinction between the larger groupings is evident everywhere we look, becoming stronger as we go up the taxonomic categories. At the higher groupings, called phyla, the differences are stark and disconnected—yet all employ the same genetic code.

Homology and analogy

A better way to discredit evolutionary theory could hardly be designed, especially considering that all the animal phyla appear suddenly in the fossil record, with no transitional forms below them. (We will look into this in more detail shortly.) Then also, we can look at the traits common to unrelated animals. Evolutionists point to the commonality of having four feet and five digits as evidence of common ancestry. With charts of a human arm shown next to a bat wing, bird wing and whale flipper, they celebrate this as strong evidence for evolution. There's no reason to believe, though, that natural selection would not have mixed things up from time to time. How come all land vertebrates have four limbs? We humans have two arms and two legs, as do many of the higher vertebrates. I am not aware of any animal species that have three limbs or five limbs. If the four limbs came about through accidental natural selection, why is four (which is actually the best arrangement) the universal number for all vertebrates with limbs? If unguided natural processes led to five fingers, why don't we see all kinds of other numbers? The similarity could just as well be explained as the result of a common design pattern rather than common ancestry by a blind evolutionary process. What's more, the designs all work! Nowhere can an evolutionist point to a design like, say, half an arm or half a wing, that is trying to evolve into something better. We see degradations, like flightless birds and blind cave fish, but those animals are not evolving in a way that supports the evolutionary story of progress from simple to complex.

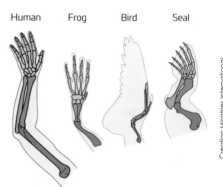

Human   Frog   Bird   Seal

Figure 4-1. **Homologous forelimbs**

Creation Ministries International

The origin of sexual reproduction

Another puzzle faces the evolutionist when considering the origin of sex. Both the plant and animal kingdoms have species that involve male and female individuals. Sex is a very important way to 'stir up' and refresh the genetic storehouse of inherited characteristics. Asexual organisms produce clones of themselves (except for the rare exceptions where there is a genetic mutation). But with sexual reproduction, there is always a blending of two sets of genes. This means that the offspring of sexually-reproducing species are unique individuals. Some biologists think this blending reduces the harmful impact of mutations, but they are not sure. Microbes seem to do quite well without sex.

It is very difficult to imagine how simple nonsexual organisms could have evolved into the two sexes we see today. Some bacteria can share genetic information by conjugation, but that is not sex. True sexuality involves a special form of cell division, called meiosis, which results in gamete cells having only one-half the normal number of chromosomes (haploid). To get sex from an asexual microbe would require several simultaneous events. First, an asexual organism would have to become 'male' in some way, and simultaneously, another would have to start becoming 'female' in some way. At the same time, there would have to be some way of reproductive exchange between these two differentiating organisms. These two incipient sexes would also have to evolve an attraction for each other.

If meiosis appeared before differentiation, how would the two haploid cells know which is which? How and why would they ever find each other and combine their genes? If meiosis appeared after differentiation, that calls for two exceedingly improbable innovations to appear independently. But even if differentiation and meiosis appeared at the same time (already an improbable happenstance beyond comprehension), sex would go nowhere without the attraction and means of sharing the chromosomes. It is unthinkable that by chance, these multiple transformations could take place from an asexual organism to pairs that had complementary sexual characteristics. A spontaneous mutation occurs so rarely, and each one is so different, that the probability of any quantity of similar transformed organisms appearing simultaneously is, statistically, far below the realm of rational consideration.

And that's just the beginning of woes for the origin of sex by accident. Once complementary organisms with sexual properties evolved through the blind processes of mutation and selection to the next level of complexity, how could a pair of organisms—one male and one female—jointly change in such a similar way so that they could continue to mate? But if they don't change, how would any new species evolve?

Mapping the history of life
Genes, trees and fossils

In recent years, scientists have been able to map the genomes of many organisms. Quite often, they find the same genetic 'toolkit' for fundamental processes in humans and fish that they find in bacteria. Evolutionists consider this to be powerful evidence for the common ancestry of all living things. A frequent scientific research activity these days is running specialized software on genomic data to map out degrees of relatedness between species and genera, resulting in so-called phylogenetic trees. Their data sets are typically limited to the smaller branches. One research team might be analyzing relationships between rodents. Another might be looking for genetic similarities between anole lizards on Caribbean islands. Another, tropical orchids. Some evolutionists compare the more distant groups: fruit flies, roundworms, and humans, for example.

Paleontologists, meanwhile, are collecting fossils, seeking to identify the dates (in millions of years) when groups are thought to have branched apart. The dream of evolutionists, using data from genetics and fossils, is to assemble a master 'tree of life' like the one Charles Darwin envisioned, showing the emergence of new species as life gradually branched out from a common trunk over the history of the earth. It would be nice for them if it were as simple as that. Unfortunately, there are serious problems when we look at the details.

The Cambrian Explosion

One difficulty comes in with a 'bang'. The first rock layers containing fossils of complex animals, called the Cambrian strata, show a profusion of new multicellular life forms and body plans. From Canada to China—all over the world—new animal types appear suddenly right above the Precambrian rocks: trilobites, worms, jellyfish, arthropods, mollusks—almost 20 entirely new animal body plans with integrated parts. Many of these marine animals exhibit compound eyes, digestive systems, circulatory systems, and nervous systems. They burrowed. They swam. They sensed their environment in ways never seen in Precambrian strata, where only simple multicellular colonies or sponges were the rule. This abrupt boundary is commonly called the 'Cambrian Explosion' by evolutionists: the biggest and most rapid diversification of major animal types in the history of life. Almost every animal alive today falls within the same major categories (known as phyla) that appeared in biology's 'big bang'.

How rapid was the Cambrian Explosion? There is some dispute among evolutionists, even using their assumed millions-of-years dates. Some of them say 20 million, some as low as 5 million. One scientist likened the fossil record to a football field. In the evolutionary timeline, one could walk from the end zone to the 60 yard line and see nothing but microbes and simple colonies of algae, with a few larger fractal-like colonies of cells unknown today. Some possible worm traces or small shelly fossils appear just before the big event. Then, in one step representing the Cambrian Explosion, about 20 new animal phyla suddenly appear. Another analogy visualizes all this explosion of animal life within 2 minutes at 9:00 p.m. on a 24-hour clock. Boom!

Figure 4-2.
Cambrian critters
From top to bottom:
Opabinia, Anomalocaris, and *Pikaia*

Stretching out the yardage or minutes in these analogies wouldn't help, because each one of the animal phyla appears abruptly without ancestors. The first trilobite, for instance, is 100% trilobite—complete with articulated limbs, compound eyes, and other body systems. Each phylum really 'exploded' onto the scene.

The Cambrian Explosion poses an immense challenge to Darwin's theory. He envisioned very gradual changes over time, not explosions of diversity in short order. According to the neo-Darwinian consensus relied on today, all the new cell types, tissues, organs and body systems must have occurred through genetic mutations filtered by natural selection. How many mutations would it take to get a trilobite? How many to get just one of its systems, like an eye, gut, or limb? When you multiply out the required mutations for the chance arrival of such complex systems, there isn't enough time in trillions of years, let alone 5 to 20 million, to reasonably expect any one of the Cambrian phyla to arrive by mutation and selection. Now add 19 more phyla, and you begin to appreciate the magnitude of the problem.

The challenge to Darwinism becomes greater when you consider that the 'innovations' that came with new body plans are organized in a hierarchical manner. It's not enough, in other words, to add a new cell type once in a while. Each new cell type (whether a nerve cell, muscle cell, or sensory cell) is organized into tissues, the tissues into organs, and the organs into systems. All the systems, moreover, must be integrated together, so that a trilobite sensing a food source can respond with its muscles, activated by nerves, to move its legs. Food requires a digestive tract, with an excretory system, all integrated so that the animal can eat and flourish.

The Cambrian Explosion was known to Darwin. He called it "the most obvious and serious objection which can be urged against the theory."[1] He could only hope that more fossil searches would reveal the missing transitional forms. Were he alive today, he would undoubtedly be dismayed to find that the problem has only gotten worse in the years since he published the *Origin of Species*. New phyla have been found showing the same abrupt appearance. Spectacular fossil-bearing outcrops of Cambrian strata in China and Canada, preserving exquisite details of eyes, legs, blood vessels, muscles, and digestive systems, have only accentuated the disparity between the Cambrian and what came before.

Nor can it be argued that the Precambrian strata were unable to preserve soft-bodied ancestral forms. Delicate sponge embryos have been found in the layers just below the Cambrian, complete with identifiable internal structures. If those could be preserved, so could the transitional forms, had they existed.

To top it off, vertebrate fish have recently been confirmed in lower Cambrian strata. The first was found in 1999 in China. Another, also in China, was reported in 2003; both of these were disputed by some evolutionists. Now, though, there can be no dispute. In late 2014, *Nature* reported discovery of a hundred spectacularly preserved vertebrate fish—complete with binocular camera-type eyes, gills, blood vessels, muscles and central nervous systems—within a recently-discovered outcrop of lower Cambrian rocks in British Columbia.[2] This puts phylum Chordata, subphylum Vertebrata, squarely within the Cambrian Explosion. (We are vertebrates, as are all other mammals, fish, birds and reptiles.) No longer can it be claimed that the Cambrian Explosion only involved simpler animals, with vertebrates evolving much later (not to imply that arthropods and other Cambrian animals were 'simple'). The paper included photos of the fossil fish with clear impressions of binocular camera eyes, livers, muscles, gills, and brains. On top of that, the Canadian specimens appear related to the earlier specimens found in China, meaning that these vertebrates were 'cosmopolitan'—world travelers. It's as if all these Cambrian animals appeared at once around the world!

Transitional fossils

At the risk of seeming to wear out poor Mr. Darwin, we should point out other facts about the fossil record that don't match his predictions. The lack of transitional forms, for instance, was famously called the 'trade secret of paleontology' by the late evolutionary paleontologist of Harvard, Stephen Jay Gould.[3] He noted that most fossil forms appear in the rock layers rather suddenly (even after the Cambrian). They remain mostly unchanged for long periods of time, and go extinct. This pattern was so ubiquitous, it led Gould and Niles Eldredge to propose an alternative to Darwinian gradualism to account for it. Called 'punctuated equilibria', their alternative scenario basically postulated that new body types sometimes evolve so fast (punctuated) that they don't leave any trace in the fossil record. Between those extraordinary times, evolution proceeds very slowly (equilibria). This hypothesis sounds, to many, like a case of 'special pleading'. As a result, it has not been popular among mainstream evolutionists. The pattern of abrupt appearance and stasis, though, remains.

Great transformations

It's true that evolutionists counter this pattern in the fossil record with some well-worn examples of evolutionary sequences. Let's look at the best-known examples.

Feathered dinosaurs

The famous bird fossil *Archaeopteryx* from Germany is often heralded as a transitional form between dinosaurs and birds. In more recent decades, dozens of newly-discovered extinct birds from China, some called 'feathered dinosaurs', have been arrayed in colorful displays purportedly showing evolution at work. It's a bit of a mystery why they all seem to come from that one area, except for the *Archaeopteryx* fossils

Figure 4-3. **Archaeopteryx**

in Germany. Some of the 'feathered dinosaurs' have been found by farmers and villagers and sold to collectors, providing income to local people. One early find was debunked as a hoax after *National Geographic* featured it prominently in their November 1999 issue. Many of the others, though, have been legitimately published in peer-reviewed journals. Evolutionists now believe they have good sequences between feathered dinosaurs and birds and between land animals and whales.

One should not think, though, that these sequences are straightforward. Many of the proposed sequences have individuals that overlap in time, leading to confusion as to what was the ancestor and what was the descendent. Some of the 'feathered dinosaurs', for instance, have been reinterpreted as secondarily flightless birds. The 'feathers' on others amount to little more than 'integumentary structures' like simple quills or fuzz, lacking the beautiful microstructure of true flight feathers. Some of the alleged 'proto-feathers' have shown up in surprising places among unrelated groups of dinosaurs, leading to talk of 'convergent evolution' (see next section). The confusing sequence has led some paleontologists to propose that some of the 'dinosaur feathers' might be artifacts of the fossilization process, like decayed collagen flaking off from the skin. Even with the currently undisputed cases, evolutionists are stuck trying to explain what the feathers were used for before flight 'evolved'. If they originated for sexual display or warmth, how did they later become 'co-opted' for flight?

Another problem with the dinosaur-to-bird sequence is that the proposed dinosaur ancestors all come from the 'lizard-hipped' dinosaurs, not the 'bird-hipped' dinosaurs. This requires another remake of a major body part to get the theory to work. Since soft parts are rarely preserved, fossils can provide only partial information about the other body systems unique to birds, such as the avian lung, fast-beating heart, and specialized digestive system.

But wait—there's more! The paleontology world was shocked in 2005 by announcements of soft tissue in dinosaur bone.[4] Soft, flexible structures resembling blood vessels (complete with blood cells) and ligaments were found inside a *T. rex* femur bone from Montana that was cut open for transport then examined in a lab. The scientists were not even looking for such things, because they assumed all soft tissues would have been replaced by rock in the 65 to 80 million years since the specimens were buried. In subsequent years, more cases have been reported, even further back in evolutionary time. Another major shock came

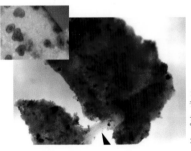

Figure 4-4. Dinosaur tissue
Soft tissue and red blood cells (inset) from a *T. rex* femur

in June 2015, when evolutionary paleontologists in the UK found original collagen protein and structures that resembled blood cells in museum specimens of dinosaur bones. Six out of eight bones examined, from both major groups of dinosaurs, gave evidence of original tissue. This led them to suspect that soft tissue may be the rule, not the exception.[5] The scientific world is still reeling from these announcements, not knowing quite what to say. Attempts to refute the evidence as secondary contamination have, so far, failed. Most scientists find it difficult to believe any tissues could survive that long. In addition, some dinosaur bones have been found with intact DNA, which should completely degenerate within 125,000 years,[6] and with carbon-14, which should be undetectable after less than 100,000 years.[7] This kind of evidence has the power to single-handedly demolish the dating scheme on which evolutionary theory relies. It will be worth watching closely.

Whales

As for whales, a few fossils can be placed in a sequence with big gaps between them, provided one is lenient with the dates and locations around the globe. Some of the fossils consist of more imagination than bone. Rare is the evolutionist willing to tackle the question of how a mouth became a blowhole, a leg became a fin, or how the sex organs moved inside the body to be cooled by specialized blood vessels in the tail fluke.[8] Echolocation in toothed whales and dolphins defies any transitional sequence. It's a multi-part, sophisticated sonar system better than anything the Navy has produced.

Evolutionists used to point to the tiny whale pelvic bones as examples of 'vestigial organs'. These, students were told, represented useless vestiges of whales' land-animal past. Recently, however, it was found that these bones have a vital role as anchors for the sex organs. They cannot be called 'vestigial' if they have a vital function in the living animals.

Tetrapods

One of the most highly-advertised transitional fossils in recent years has been *Tiktaalik*, an alleged transitional form between fish and land animals from Canada. Discoverer Neil Shubin wrote a book, *Your Inner Fish*, and appeared on TV specials promoting his fossil. Unfortunately for him, tetrapod tracks allegedly millions of years older than *Tiktaalik* were subsequently found in Poland, casting doubt on his claim.[9]

Figure 4-5. **Tiktaalik**

Horses

A century ago, the famous 'horse series' was popular in textbooks and museum displays, offering undisputed proof of evolution. These days, that sequence has been largely discredited. The current view of 'horse evolution' looks more like a bush than a tree, with different species branching out on different continents with no apparent progress. This example alone should offer a stern lesson to all us critical thinkers: we should take today's popularized accounts of 'great transformations' with a heavy dose of skepticism.

Figure 4-6.
Tetrapod trackway
Limestone slab with fossil
footprints older than Tiktaalik

Piotr Szrek, Uppsala University

The simplified views in museums and TV documentaries often lag behind current thinking in the scientific journals.

Problems with Neo-Darwinism

Lack of foresight

It must be kept in mind that the mutation-selection process has no foresight. Each mutation is a single, mindless occurrence, oblivious to what came before or after. A 'beneficial' mutation might remove a beetle's wings on a windy island, keeping it from being blown out into the sea, but mutations cannot plan ahead to create novel structures or new genetic information. Mutations are simply copying mistakes. They cannot produce the encyclopedic quantities of coherent genetic information necessary to go from simple to complex, no matter how much time is allowed. Whatever benefit might be provided by a chance mutation, it must be valuable to the organism when it occurs—so much so, that the individual possessing it survives and all the others in the population perish. Moreover, the mutation must occur in the gametes, which implies that the offspring, not the individual mutant, enjoys the benefit. A mutation cannot sit waiting for other mutations to arrive so that it can become a sonar organ, or blowhole, or flipper; most likely, it would be eliminated by natural selection long before a second beneficial mutation arrived.

Mutational load

Remember, too, the vast majority of mutations are harmful or near-neutral. Evolutionists speak of 'mutational load' being a burden on the genome. In many cases, cells have the ability to correct the mistakes. Those that cannot be corrected often cause serious problems or death. Geneticists can identify hundreds of severe human illnesses caused by mutations. Neutral mutations, as the name implies, may not cause harm immediately, but they accumulate like typos in a book, degrading the information and gradually making it less readable. If mutations are the seed plot of evolutionary innovation, why do cells try so hard to eliminate them?

Mutations that might appear beneficial in one gene can have damaging effects on other genes. We can see why this is so when considering man-made complex systems, like automobiles. The failure of a governor in an engine might allow the vehicle to run faster, but this 'benefit' will likely cause another component to overheat or wear out faster. The risk is even higher in a dynamic, networked, signal processing system like a cell. Molecular biologists have found many instances where a mutation on one gene affects a distant gene on another chromosome. We know from experience that it's dangerous to tamper with integrated systems. How much more to do it in a random, blind way!

When pressed, evolutionists have a hard time providing examples of any beneficial mutations that add new genetic information. One favorite is the mutation that produces sickle-cell anemia, because it provides some protection against malaria. If evolutionists can only illustrate their theory by celebrating a mutation that causes a deadly disease to help against another deadly disease, their theory is in trouble.

Another oft-cited example is the 'evolution' of antibiotic resistance. But as Dr Michael Behe showed in his second book, *The Edge of Evolution*, this kind of benefit comes about by breaking things. He uses the analogy of trench warfare: "If the enemy can be stopped or slowed by burning your own bridges and bombing your own radio towers and oil refineries, then away they go," he says "Darwinian trench warfare does not lead to progress—it leads back to the Stone Age."[10] None of these 'beneficial mutations' add new genetic information capable of assembling new organs, body plans or complex systems like powered flight or echolocation.

The only cause we know capable of envisioning a distant goal and organizing parts to reach that goal is intelligence. The lack of foresight is the major problem with the Darwinian mechanism. We should not accept dismissive, sweeping accounts that claim 'whales evolved from land animals' or 'birds evolved from dinosaurs' without asking these kinds of serious questions.

Environmental selection

Evolutionists often say that the environment selects the best adapted. The environment cannot be a selector, though, because it is inanimate. Nothing in the environment forces an animal to 'evolve to' anything. For instance, the statement that 'birds evolved to fly' makes no sense in Neo-Darwinism. There's nothing about air that forces any animal to fly. Rocks don't sprout wings just because if they don't they will fall off a cliff. If air or the environment made an animal 'evolve to' fly, then every animal would fly—it would be a law of nature.

Nor is it meaningful to allege that 'if a bird didn't evolve wings, it wouldn't fly.' This begs the question of evolution by assuming evolution's creative power in the first place. What we observe are birds already possessing the sophisticated equipment and integrated systems for flight. In our common-sense experience, we know that every machine able to fly with controlled, powered flight was designed. The only difference is that man-made flying craft, whether airplanes, helicopters, or drones, pale in comparison to the design in a bird—the ultimate flying machine. If our best efforts were intelligently designed, is it logical to assume that superior 'natural' examples were not?

An evolutionary paper in the *Proceedings of the National Academy of Sciences* made this observation:

> Even the most seasoned students of evolution, starting with Darwin himself, have occasionally expressed amazement that the mechanism of natural selection has produced the whole of Life as we see it around us. There is a computational way to articulate the same amazement: "What algorithm could possibly achieve all this in a mere three and a half billion years?[11]

The authors could only propose a solution by cheating: imagining that natural selection is like a computer algorithm. Evolution, they said, is like an algorithm that explores the environment and adapts to it automatically. Natural selection is no such thing. It is blind, aimless, and thoughtless. Evolution could not care less whether a living thing adapts or goes extinct. And the laws of nature ensure that it will go extinct, if it were not for abundant, built-in repair mechanisms that fix most of the mistakes that 'natural processes' throw at them. Even these evolutionists had to wonder if billions of years was enough time. Time is not a solution on a bad route. If you're trying to walk north on an iceberg moving south, adding more time is not going to get you to the North Pole.

Convergent evolution

But now, we must watch the evolutionists multiply their miracles! Frequently in the living world we find independent groups of organisms possessing the same design solution. There are extinct marine reptiles, for instance, that looked like tuna, apparently swimming just as efficiently. The octopus has no evolutionary relationship to humans, but our eyes are similar in many respects. Dolphins and bats (both mammals) are only distantly related, evolutionists believe, but both employ sophisticated echolocation systems. And flight—that paragon of a demanding physical capability—had to evolve independently four times—in insects, birds, extinct reptiles (pterosaurs), and mammals (bats). This is the challenge of 'convergent evolution'—and like 'living fossils' we'll talk about in the next section, it is a pervasive problem.

Evolutionists basically respond to this problem with word games. They say that organs are 'homologous' if they are similar and related by common descent, but only 'analogous' if they are similar but not related by common descent. This clever scheme allows them to have it both ways: if organs are homologous, they evolved, but if they are analogous, they evolved. The similarities, however, can be extremely close—sometimes too hard to distinguish except to a specialist. For instance, there are marine bivalves that look very similar even though they belong to different phyla. Some unrelated plant families happened to arrive at nearly identical leaf patterns. In the animal kingdom, we find repeated 'convergent evolution' of prehensile tails, webbed feet, and cusped teeth. Then there are the marsupials, many of which have very similar-looking placental-mammal counterparts, even though the two groups supposedly split apart long before the adaptations appeared. The phenomenon of convergence can be extended all the way down to the gene level in some instances.

Calling this phenomenon 'convergent evolution' of 'analogous' structures amounts to inventing terms to distract attention from a very real empirical challenge to Neo-Darwinism. It almost gets humorous at times. For instance, evolutionists with all seriousness have alleged that flight among stick insects evolved not just once, but four times independently.

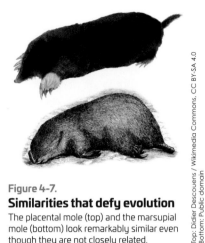

Figure 4-7.
Similarities that defy evolution
The placental mole (top) and the marsupial mole (bottom) look remarkably similar even though they are not closely related.

Upon hearing that, one evolutionist exclaimed four times in a row, "Impossible!" Other evolutionists reclassified web-building spiders into two unrelated groups, concluding that orb web weaving evolved twice. A recent paper alleges that geckos evolved the ability to climb smooth surfaces eleven times, and lost it nine times. A recent major revision to the 'tree of life' requires believing that nervous systems evolved separately in two different phyla.

Think of the number of near-miraculous mutational events that would be required to account for just one instance, let alone multiple instances, of these complex traits. One might conclude it would take far more faith to believe in 'convergent evolution' than in common design. If a single designer wanted to illustrate unity of design while falsifying universal common descent, he could hardly have found a better way to do it.

Problems with fossils

Living fossils and Lazarus taxa

Another problem is actually quite interesting, and once again, very damaging to Mr. Darwin's proposal. It is the problem of 'living fossils'. Darwin envisioned a world in flux. Everything should be in a condition of gradual change—descent with modification, he called it—with each organism developing new traits over time through the accumulation of slight variations. How the variations come about is beside the point. We would predict, from Darwin's view of the world, that nothing stays the same, given enough time. Living fossils mess up this picture.

There are organisms that disappeared from the fossil record, sometimes millions of years ago, it is said, only to reappear alive and well in some part of the world. The coelacanth (a fish with bony fins) is a classic example—thought to be long extinct before the dinosaurs vanished. To some evolutionists a century ago, it looked like it was on the way to developing limbs. But then, to their great surprise, a living coelacanth was found swimming off the coast of Madagascar in 1938. Many coelacanths have been found alive since, their bony fins having nothing to do with walking on land.

Examples of living fossils abound. There's a reptile called the tuatara that was thought to have gone extinct during the age of dinosaurs, but it lives today in south

**Figure 4-8.
Coelacanth**

New Zealand. Australia has the Wollemi pine; China has the Dawn Redwood and Ginkgo tree. Dozens of other examples are known. Some evolutionists have given the name 'Lazarus taxa' to these surprisingly lively organisms—as if they miraculously rose from

the dead. After chuckling at the term, we should ask if it is plausible to believe that millions of years actually went by without any of them leaving a trace in the fossil record. Could there be something wrong with the dates? And if they endured so many millions of years somewhere hidden around the world, why are they virtually identical to the fossil forms?

Remarkable stasis

Figure 4-9. **Wollemi pine**

A similar problem arises when we consider examples of 'remarkable stasis'— organisms that apparently got off of Darwin's conveyor belt of gradual change and decided to just live in place, unevolved, for up to hundreds of millions of years. Horseshoe crabs look pretty much the same as they did during the Ordovician. Living comb jellies look identical to those found in the Cambrian Explosion—some fossil forms were even more complex, sporting armor that none have today. The same story applies to many other living things. We might well ask how microbes, which divide frequently and should evolve quickly, missed the evolutionary train, remaining pretty much the same as when they first appeared on earth billions of years ago. Are we to believe that things evolve except when they don't? A theory that purports to explain opposite things with equal ease does not sound like a good scientific theory. Such a theory could explain anything.

Tree of life—or forest?

The lack of conformity between evidence and theory has some evolutionists willing to jettison the concept of a universal 'tree of life'. Some have proposed a 'ring of life' or a 'network of life' or other metaphors. Probably the best description is an orchard. If we can imagine young trees sprouting up together and splitting into small branches, we can better simulate the picture of the fossil record: multiple body plans appear simultaneously, then diverge a bit after that, but never join up or change from one branch into another branch. These are radical revisions to the Darwinian picture of natural history that has ruled the world for over 157 years.

The intelligent alternative

How can the observations be explained outside of Neo-Darwinism? In a recent best seller, *Darwin's Doubt*, Dr Stephen Meyer argued that the Cambrian Explosion not only falsifies Darwinian evolution, but provides positive evidence for intelligent design. Most evolutionists took deep offense at this explanation, claiming it was unscientific (it appears many of the critics did not even read the book). One knowledgeable expert on the Cambrian Explosion did read it, and offered his idea of how the explosion occurred. He suggested that mutations to *gene regulatory networks* (GRNs) might have been responsible for rapid diversification of animal types. As Meyer explained in an appendix in the paperback edition, though, such an explanation begs the question of the origin of the regulatory networks in the first place. Moreover, everything we know about GRNs suggests they cannot tolerate mutations. Like tampering with master switches in a factory, experiments show that modifying a GRN as an animal develops has catastrophic downstream effects, usually leading to the death of the organism. Such a proposal, additionally, does nothing to explain the many unique genes found in the Cambrian animals. In short, the origin of the genetic information for the Cambrian body types remains a serious challenge to Neo-Darwinism or any other unguided process.

In Meyer's previous book, *Signature in the Cell*, he made a similar argument for the origin of life: the information is best explained by intelligent design. The argument is even more compelling prior to life's origin, because natural selection would be unavailable before a self-sustaining, heritable cell existed. In both cases, the amount of new genetic information required vastly exceeds the capabilities of chance, natural selection, or any other unguided process. From our uniform experience with complex systems, Meyer argues, there is only one cause we know capable of producing such systems. That cause is intelligence. The inference to the best explanation, therefore, is that intelligence played a role in the appearance of cells and animal body plans.

In the next chapter we will examine how some scientists attempt to explain the origin of life by undirected causes without the aid of natural selection.

ENDNOTES

1. Darwin, C., *On the Origin of Species*, 5th Ed, Murray, p. 346, 1869.
2. Morris, S.C. and Caron, J.B., A primitive fish from the Cambrian of North America, *Nature* **512**:419–422, 28 August 2014, doi:10.1038/nature13414.
3. See Bates, G., That quote!—about the missing transitional fossils, creation.com/pq.
4. Wieland, C., Still soft and stretchy, 25 March 2005, creation.com/stretchy.
5. Bertazzo, *et al.*, Fibres and cellular structures preserved in 75-million–year-old dinosaur specimens, *Nature Communications* **6**:7352, 2015, doi: 10.1038/ncomms8352.
6. Sarfati, J., DNA and bone cells found in dinosaur bone, 11 Dec 2012, creation.com/dino-dna.
7. Wieland, C., Radiocarbon in dino bones, 22 Jan 2013, creation.com/dinoC14.
8. The challenges to Darwinian evolution of the whale's reproductive system and echolocation are illustrated in the Illustra Media film *Living Waters: Intelligent Design in the Oceans of the Earth*.
9. Walker, T., Tetrapods from Poland trample the *Tiktaalik* school of evolution, 14 January 2010, creation.com/tetrapod-footprints.
10. Behe, M., *The Edge of Evolution*, Free Press, p. 43, 2007.
11. Chastain, *et al.*, Algorithms, games, and evolution, *Proceedings of the National Academy of Sciences* **111**(29):10620, 16 June 2014, doi: 10.1073/pnas.1406556111.

5

Populating
the Spacecraft

L ife on earth had to start somewhere. Most evolutionary accounts choose to start with single-celled organisms, so let us think about that for a minute. Many people have peered through a microscope in biology class or at home looking at a simple animal called an amoeba. A drop of stagnant water on a microscope slide reveals a variety of creatures, but the amoeba looks the simplest—just a blob of stuff moving about slowly, sending out finger-like projections in the way it wants to go. The simplicity is an illusion, however; biologists classify it as a eukaryote, or microbe with a nucleus. Eukaryotes are thought to be more highly evolved than prokaryotes, like bacteria. But even the simpler prokaryotes can propel themselves through water, and all single-celled organisms have the fascinating capacity to divide into two identical cells. What led to the appearance of such miniature marvels on Spacecraft Earth?

Design requirements

In thinking about the necessities for life on earth or on other planets, origin-of-life researchers usually consider three things necessary: metabolism, a genetic code, and a membrane. Metabolism is needed to extract energy from the environment in a sustainable way. A genetic code is needed to preserve the information about the cell's workings, so that it can be passed on. And a membrane—

or some other container—is needed to keep the contents of the organism from spilling out and becoming lost to the surroundings. Could these requirements all come together at one place and time?

The difficulty of imagining life coming together spontaneously increases when we observe how living organisms meet these three requirements. Metabolic reactions, even in the simplest organism, are highly complex, and they are regulated by numerous feedback controls that form elaborate reaction networks. Genetic codes in the simplest microbes contain large amounts of specific information for how proteins, enzymes and other essential molecules are to be constructed and regulated; these genes are, in turn, regulated by proteins and enzymes coded for in the genetic code. (This is a classic 'chicken and egg' problem—which came first?) Finally, cell membranes are much more complicated than simple storage sacks. They control which molecules can come in and go out, often against what would take place naturally by the laws of diffusion and osmosis.

From the bottom up

Since the gap between non-life and life as we know it is such a big one, scientists often try to start with a simpler problem: how did earth produce the 'building blocks of life'—the simpler molecules that might have been used to construct a living cell? Presumably— the thinking goes—if one gets building blocks, a building can't be far behind. Of special interest are amino acids, the building blocks of proteins. Since proteins make up the bulk of cells, finding naturally-occurring amino acids is thought to have helped 'bootstrap' a sterile world up the first steps toward a living organism.

There has been highly-publicized laboratory work indicating that it is possible to produce amino acids by electrical discharges through mixtures of fundamental gases. Simple gases such as methane, hydrogen, ammonia, and water vapor are common in space and were long thought to exist in earth's atmosphere before life appeared. In 1953, Stanley Miller, a grad student of Harold Urey, used electrical discharges in closed gas tubes to simulate lightning in the primitive earth atmosphere. He did, in fact, generate a number of amino acids, along with a variety of other organic compounds. The experiment electrified not only the gases, but the news media as well: reporters went wild with stories that the 'building blocks of life' had been produced under plausible early-earth conditions. Illustrations of the

Miller Experiment are a staple in high school textbooks. Since then, amino acids and other organic compounds have been found in meteorites.

The ingredients

What is an organic compound? The name implies that it has some connection with living matter. However, the field of organic chemistry is defined as a sub-branch of chemistry dealing with compounds containing

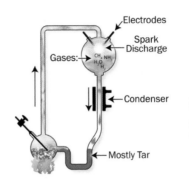

Figure 5-1.
Miller-Urey experiment
Formed organic compounds, but came nowhere close to creating life

carbon. Due to its ease of linking up with other elements, carbon can give rise to an extremely large number of organic compounds. Quite a few organic compounds have been found in space, leading some to speculate that life may be common on planets around other stars. This has given rise to a whole new science called *astrobiology*, the science of life beyond earth. The problem is, most organic compounds have nothing to do with life. Many, in fact, are deadly poisons, like cyanide and the BPA that government regulators have banned from plastics. It's not enough to create organic compounds, then; they must be the right type, or they can cause more harm than good. As for life in space—well, let's just say astrobiologists are still looking.

An organic compound—even a vital one for an organism, like an amino acid—is not a living thing. Life forms, however, are made up of organic compounds. All the molecules in living cells are either organic compounds themselves, are manufactured from organic compounds, or are utilized by them (e.g., salt). But a living cell is much more than any of these. You can put all the building blocks together in the right amounts, and still not have life. Scientists have a hard time defining life, but most consider several very special properties in their definitions: (1) controlled use of energy, taking in nutrients and discarding waste; (2) some sort of locomotion; (3) the ability to reproduce. One astrobiologist offered this concise definition: "life reproduces, and life uses energy. These functions follow a set of instructions embedded within the organism."[1] I like this definition because of its focus on instructions, or information.

The instructions

Every organism we know of has a 'handbook' of information for its own development, its own characteristics, and its future. That handbook is written in molecules, just like an encyclopedia is written in letters. Life's genetic code is written in a long molecule called DNA (deoxyribonucleic acid), looking something like a twisted ladder, or double helix. The individual segments of the DNA chain, called *nucleotides*, contain *bases* labeled A, C, T, and G. These comprise the letters of this encyclopedia. Taken together, they store the information required to synthesize the building blocks into larger molecules (proteins, fats and sugars) that determine the characteristics of the organism as it develops and maintains itself. When it comes time for reproduction, all that information is duplicated precisely to allow the establishment of another similar organism. We should take note that without very precise replication, the genetic information would quickly erode away in what is called 'error catastrophe' in a few generations. That is why cells go to great lengths to proofread their genetic information and correct errors.

Figure 5-2. DNA
Instructions written using four chemical 'letters':
A, C, T, and G

Bigstock

So as we see, a living cell is far more than only a collection of building blocks, just like a car is more than a collection of parts wrapped up together in a sack. In fact, we might say that information, rather than molecules, is the real 'stuff' of life. Information builds and controls the membrane, cell wall, or 'skin' that forms the outer boundary of the organism, regulating its permeability so as to allow nutrients to enter and waste products to exit. Information builds the proteins that give structure to the cell, and the enzymes that control its metabolism. And information—stored instructions—is the essence of the DNA code. Life is all about information, from bottom up, top down and inside out.

It is very difficult, therefore, to imagine how an assortment of even the right 'building blocks' could be brought together correctly without the guidance of information at a very high level. We certainly never observe that happening in any other information-rich, functioning system. The problem for evolutionists is not so much to find the building blocks, but to explain how they were assembled in an informational way, so as to be able to simultaneously have a membrane, a genetic code, and a metabolic network. To speculate that it happened, by accident, in a random collection of naturally occurring organic chemicals, would surely qualify as one of the most remarkable, improbable events that could be imagined in the entire universe. For all intents and purposes, it would be a miracle. Even the finest of organic chemists, in the most sophisticated laboratories, with the greatest stock of organic compounds at their disposal, have never been able to synthesize a life form from scratch. Not even close!

Charles Darwin didn't write in his famous books about how life originated. Once, though, in a letter to a friend, he imagined a "warm little pond" with organic compounds and chemical salts where they might come together fortuitously into a simple organism without design. But he never developed the idea, and the complexity of life was little appreciated in his day. His phrase gave rise to the popular myth of the 'primordial soup' where life might have emerged. In recent years, astrobiologists have expanded the search for building blocks of life to gas clouds, meteorites, or deep under the sea in hydrothermal vents. The problem with each of these 'scenarios' as they are called is that they do not explain the origin of the information required for "functions [that] follow a set of instructions embedded within the organism".

If life could emerge from the right chemicals without the benefit of information, we might expect it to emerge in many natural environments today. There are all sorts of mixtures of organic and other chemicals in laboratories, waste collection tanks, sewer collection and treatment basins all around the world, some much more complete and enriched with organic compounds than the 'primordial soup'. Why have none of these ever been shown to produce a new living cell? Why does a higher order organic system not spontaneously appear in these simple mixtures?

To amplify the point, imagine killing a cell in a test tube, letting all its parts leak out. Would anyone ever expect natural causes to put that Humpty Dumpty back together again? We know intuitively it would never happen, even with all the parts for a cell present, in the right proportions, and in close contact. It should be the best case scenario, because the cell was once alive. The late organic chemist, Dr A.E. Wilder-Smith, gave another pithy illustration using a sardine can. Everything for life is present, because the sardines were once alive. You can heat the can, bump the can, and add energy in any way you wish, but the sardines will not come back to life, because they are on the path of decay. More importantly, no new life form will emerge from the ingredients. If anyone ever thought for a moment that a novel organism could spontaneously appear in one of the millions of sealed sardine cans around the world, the food industry would panic, never being able to predict what new life would emerge in our canned foods. But then insert the genetic information and machinery for *E. coli* into the sardine can, and it would literally explode with life! The difference is information.

High hurdles

We must understand that the information content in life is exceedingly high. Consider, for instance, the matter of chemical synthesis, which is the focus of a huge industry. Let us look at the makeup of just one small portion of a bacterial cell wall. The chemical structural formula is reproduced in Figure 5-3.

One can see immediately the large number of carbon-carbon bonds that are involved (In Figure 5-3, there are carbon atoms at the junctions of each short line—dozens and dozens of them, which organic chemists omit to simplify a structural formula). I am sure that the full pattern of a cell membrane has this structure repeated thousands of times. Carbon atoms in organic compounds do not just

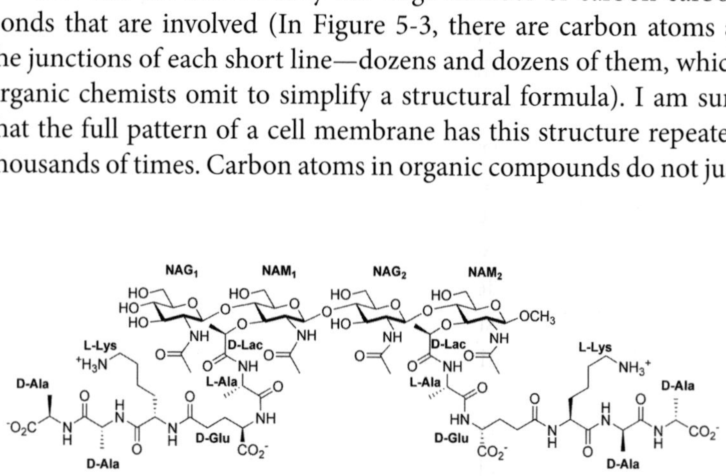

Figure 5-3. Cellular architecture
The molecular structure of a portion of a bacterial cell wall

'stick together.' They require overcoming very real binding energies. It requires special lab procedures for scientists to get even two to join. For millions of atoms to come together in just the right combination and order would take an infinite amount of trial and error, if it would even be possible to make all the chemical bonds stick together.

I spent one summer in my college days working in an experimental acetylene plant in Los Angeles where we took natural gas (methane, CH_4) and repeatedly passed it through a hot furnace, back and forth until some combination took place. The first product was ethane, C_2H_6, a simple two-carbon molecule. Even so, the yield was only a few percent after the first few passes. It took a temperature pushing one thousand degrees and a stone catalyst face, and even then, only a few percent combined. It is highly unlikely that simple methane molecules, at plausible surface conditions on a primitive earth, would combine into higher-level organic compounds, without energetic radiation like lightning or UV radiation. Even then, the yield would be very low, diluted to vanishingly small concentrations in the vast oceans. But then, to imagine all the combinations that would have to take place to build the molecular fabric of a cell wall— only a portion of which is shown by the above structural formula— well, the improbabilities quickly multiply into impossibilities.

Ignition

But suppose chance (or even, if you wish, a skilled scientist) could somehow carefully craft and assemble all of the components that constitute a cell: the membrane molecules, DNA molecules, and all the proteins used in metabolism, everything—all in their correct concentrations, and placed in the right arrangement. There is one additional ingredient that is totally beyond the comprehension of mankind: it is what we call LIFE. The initiation of life in a cell that has been accidentally or purposely assembled is something that we do not understand. What characteristic allows an assemblage of organic chemicals to exhibit life behavior? How did this first cell somehow get jumpstarted into being alive? Even if one assumes that the first cell emerged from a random combination of chemicals coming together in the right sequence, it cannot explain this vital factor. Getting the parts right does not explain them proceeding to fly into action, metabolizing energy sources, running all of the internal mechanisms and, for the first time, reproducing all the parts faithfully.

What is this spark of life? When life is gone from the cell, it is gone, period! Undoubtedly, the best scenario for seeing life emerge spontaneously is the one where life has just departed for some reason, like in the test tube we described with a cell that has been ripped open. All of the right ingredients are there, the membrane, the DNA, the metabolic proteins. But we know that life does not spontaneously regenerate itself and start again, even though all the necessary factors are present, in the right place, in the right sequence, and in the right amount. Why? There is something unique about life itself that transcends all of the chemical forms, shapes and building blocks from which it is constructed.

Bewildering complexity

Up to this point, we have greatly oversimplified a living cell. Proteins, for instance, are not just simple chains of amino acids. They are, rather, very highly ordered, folded structures that work like molecular machines. Some of them actually have multiple moving parts with lever arms, pulleys, and rotating wheels. If it were possible to magnify a cell to the size of a warehouse, instead of seeing it as a speck under the microscope, we would behold a remarkable factory of molecular machines working and interacting in marvelous ways. Some scientific websites have animated portions of the cell in all their glory, allowing viewers to witness the remarkable inner life of the cell. One can see the membrane with its orderly gates controlling traffic in and out of the cell and nucleus. One can see protein transporters with legs, walking and carrying vessels on monorail tracks. One can see other parts repelling invaders, or repairing and recycling other machines. Inside the nucleus, one can witness machines transcribing DNA and sending the transcripts to machines outside the nucleus where the code is translated into proteins. It's a dazzling spectacle!

There is no 'simple' part to a cell. Consider just the cell membrane. Much of it consists of a bilayer of lipid molecules, but embedded throughout it are specialized gates that control what enters and exits. These gates are highly specific. Some can let sodium ions in, but not potassium ions, which are not much different in size. Some let tiny water molecules in against the concentration gradient. Then there is a process called endocytosis, in which portions of the membrane surround outside cargo to form a vesicle that pinches off and carries its contents into the interior. In some types of endocytosis, proteins in the shape of a triskelion form beautiful miniature geodesic domes around these vesicles as they form, then disperse for re-use. Most cells have a tiny 'antenna' called a cilium embedded in the cell membrane. Inside this cilium, molecular trucks carry cargo up and down the stalks in a highly controlled manner to maintain the

Figure 5-4. Cargo cage
During endocytosis, individual triskelion-shaped clathrin proteins (cyan) combine to create this geodesic dome (blue) which transports material into the cell interior.

cilium's length. It all seems like something out of a science fiction movie about a highly-advanced alien civilization, but it's real. This is going on right now in every cell of your body.

Following regulations

Cells grow from within under tight control. When they reach a certain size, the process of cell division is switched on. The so-called *cell cycle* is regulated by a series of checkpoints. Every base of DNA, every 'letter' of the genetic code, is faithfully copied onto two strands inside the nucleus. Molecular 'proofreading' machines ensure that no 'typos' are made in the many millions of letters. Errors are detected and quickly corrected, resulting in an accuracy exceeding that of the best human typists. When the entire code has been duplicated, more molecular machines begin winding up the DNA onto spools called chromatin. These coil up into dense packages that coil again, and again, in supercoils, forming the familiar chromosomes—the most densely packed and elaborately organized form of information in the known universe!

Figure 5-5. DNA packaging
Chromosomes are made of super-coiled DNA.

Once the chromosomes are complete, the nuclear wall breaks down, and the chromosomes line up, each one facing its copy. A spindle of molecular strands latches onto each chromosome. Then, powerful molecular motors winch them apart. Simultaneously, a molecular winch surrounding the entire cell contracts, pinching the cell in half. The result is two daughter cells, each with its full complement of DNA.

This is but a brief snapshot of what takes place within a single cell. The number of chemical and physical processes required to sustain life, to grow, and to divide can fill many textbooks.

It is only within our lifetimes that biological science has been able to begin to understand, unravel, and examine these processes of life at the molecular level. They bear all the hallmarks of sophisticated man-made systems, like factories or computer networks, except for one thing: they are light-years ahead of anything man has been able to create. Is it rational to imagine cells being products of blind, unguided processes?

Much more could be written beyond this simplistic description of a cell. To appreciate the complexity visually, I highly recommend a video put out by Illustra Media entitled *Origin*.[2] With stunning animations, the film illustrates the improbability of chance assembling the proteins, nucleic acids and other components that would have to come together at the same place and time for the first cell. Portions of the film can be seen at the website indicated in the footnote.

A necessary and sufficient cause

In recent years, a growing minority of scientists, unsatisfied with the usual naturalistic explanations, has focused on the information content of life as something that cannot be dismissively overlooked or explained away. Noting that every information-rich functional system we know of had an intelligent cause, they ask, why not use the same reasoning for biology? One would never enter a working factory and attribute it to natural causes, like wind or explosions. In the same way, they argue, a living cell is best explained by an intelligent cause rather than an unguided cause, like natural selection. Since *intelligent design* is commonly used as an explanatory inference in other sciences, such as in forensics, cryptology, and archaeology, it should apply in biology, too. One of their favorite examples is a tiny molecular machine found in a 'simple' bacterium.

Molecular machines

That machine is called a flagellum. The bacterial flagellum is a rotary outboard motor only 45 nm (nanometers—45 billionths of a meter) in diameter. Many bacteria have one or more of these machines to move them around in liquid. The rotor and stator, anchored inside the cell wall, drive a long thin helical filament that extends several cell body lengths outside the cell into the external watery medium. Some bacteria, like the *E. coli* that lives in your gut, have several of these motors that work together in synchrony. The *E.coli* bacterium has a single, circular chromosome consisting of a single double-stranded chain of DNA about 700 times longer than the body of the cell. It contains 4,639,221 base pairs specifying 2,488 genes. Among these genes are codes for at least 40 proteins that make up the flagellum.

A Harvard microbiologist who has studied the bacterial flagellum for years called it the most efficient machine in the universe.

Some of these rotary engines spin as fast as 24,000 rpm, but can stop in less than a quarter turn and reverse direction. The flagellum looks and works like an outboard motor. For all practical purposes, it *is* an outboard motor—except that it is much more sophisticated, efficient, and reliable than any rotary motor man has designed.

Figure 5-6. Bacterial flagellum
This organelle is powered by an amazing rotary outboard motor which can spin at 24,000 rpm.

This is found, remember, in one of the simplest organisms of all—one closest to the presumed origin of life!

Were we to come across such a machine a billion times larger than a flagellum, we would not hesitate for a second to attribute it to intelligent design. So why not here? Only a philosophical bias would prevent a rational mind from using the very same reasoning in this case.

There's another rotary engine even smaller than the flagellum. Called ATP synthase, this molecular machine, only 20 billionths of a meter tall, powers every living thing, from bacteria to humans, by

Illustra Media / Unlocking the Mystery of Life film

taking a flow of protons to run a drive shaft that manufactures ATP, the energy currency of cells. On an active day, your cells can produce your body's weight in ATP. Our bodies have quadrillions of these engines, running at over 9,000 rpm with near 100% efficiency, keeping us alive.[3] How could such a marvel evolve?

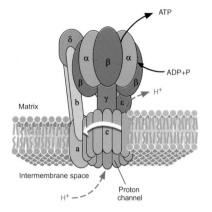

Figure 5-7. Miniature motor
This tiny motor manufactures ATP, a molecule that powers life.

Chance all the way up?

Moving beyond the question of origin, let us try and imagine how a simple, one-celled organism could be transformed into higher forms of life.

Let us start with that single, one-celled organism that somehow spontaneously appeared out of the primordial soup. What causes an organism to change? The standard answer since the beginning of the 20th century has been mutation. Mutations are mistakes in the genetic instructions of an organism, namely, in its DNA.

One frequent cause of mutations is ionizing radiation. Before our oxygen atmosphere appeared to filter most of it out, the main source of high energy radiation that would have been around when this one-celled organism came into existence would be the ultraviolet radiation from the sun, and cosmic radiation from deep space.

Cosmic rays are very disruptive bundles of high energy. These days, because of our atmosphere, ozone layer and magnetic field, we are protected from the worst cosmic rays and solar rays, but some still get through. When they collide with an atom or a molecule in an organism's DNA, they can break the chemical bonds in very destructive ways, even breaking DNA strands apart, leading to death of the cell. Fortunately, many breaks can be repaired quickly by molecular machines. We stay out of the sun because of the potential damage from ionizing radiation in the form of ultraviolet light from the sun. But on rare occasions, could ionizing radiation lead to improvements for our simple cell?

In my undergraduate days at Caltech, I took the genetics course, and one of our main activities there was producing and studying mutations in fruit flies. We would begin by placing fruit fly eggs in a Petri dish; then, we would send these off for irradiation by the X-ray department. When our batches of eggs hatched, we would study the characteristics of the adult fruit flies whose eggs had been exposed to the X-rays. Many of those flies looked grotesque. One fruit fly, for instance, would have one eye one color and the other eye a different color. Another fly would have one eye missing entirely. Another one would have a missing leg or a missing wing, or an extra leg or wing. On occasion, there would be a leg sticking out where the antenna should be. All of the mutations I ever saw were destructive. I am sure that 99.99% of all mutations are harmful. In fact, I never saw any mutation that 'improved' a fruit fly in any conceivable way. This has been the uniform experience of all fruit fly researchers since the 1930s, when irradiation experiments began. The closest thing to an 'advance' has been a fruit fly with four wings. Trouble is, it cannot fly! The extra wings were not attached to muscles, and so acted as impediments to fitness.

Evolutionary theory invests great hope in mutations. Rare beneficial mutations are said to be the raw material for natural selection, or what Darwin later called the 'survival of the fittest' (borrowing Herbert Spencer's phrase). In the modern theory called Neo-Darwinism (which attributes variation to genetic mutations), good mutations are thought to accumulate by natural selection. If and when a beneficial mutation appears that in some way makes the organism more 'fit' in the competitive struggle for existence, that benefit will outcompete other organisms and will be transmitted to the offspring. It is surmised that even a minor change in the organism could produce this competitive advantage and therefore result in greater survivability, and more effective propagation, so that the change, over time, would dominate.

Rethinking Darwin's solution

We all learned this story in school, because it is the only theory taught in biology these days. Many textbooks illustrate it with the giraffe. If one giraffe somehow developed a neck a little longer than the rest of the herd because of a mutation, that giraffe could reach higher in a tree to get more food. As a result, it would have a better chance of surviving than those with shorter necks. (How it reached the food before becoming an adult is left to speculation.) Its progeny would presumably inherit longer necks, too—also with better survivability. Applying this principle to my little dish of fruit flies, I could not identify any attribute that would have given any mutant an edge over the rest in terms of better survivability. As a matter of fact, all of the mutants had a much shorter survival time than the ones not exposed to radiation.

And, so now, back to our one-celled rudimentary creature swimming the primordial seas; it is difficult to see how a mutation could lead toward multicellular life. Did ionizing radiation cause two cells to stick together? How, then would that be passed on to the offspring? What benefit would it provide? It would seem to slow both of them down, not help them.

Of course, one has to move well beyond two cells to get to an organism able to have differentiated functions, but only at that point would multicellularity seem to offer a benefit. As one goes up the order of complexity in simple organisms, some of the next things that begin to appear are small colonies of cells with hair-like projections called cilia (these look simple, but actually are as complex as flagella). In developing these cilia, think about the problem of getting them to move in a cooperative way so as to propel the cell through the fluid instead of beating about randomly. It would be a remarkable thing to see coordinated cilia appear by mutation in one cell alone, but to get a colony of cells to do so challenges the imagination.

A question I will be continually asking throughout this treatise is this: how much luck can you reasonably expect at one time? If somehow this simple one-celled organism suddenly developed cilia, and if we depend on lucky mutations to take care of other requirements, such as a means of synchronizing the cilia, how did the organism survive before both appeared? The movement is necessary to move the cell in the fluid to allow feeding, and to refresh the fluid around the membrane. One cannot have the structure without the function, so how many simultaneous lucky mutations were required?

Was the primordial soup edible?

The next question to ponder is what this first one-celled organism lived on. Today, there are many nutrients in the seas and terrestrial water sources. The world is rich with organic molecules readily available, such as sugars, carbohydrates, and even proteins. However, these were all produced by living organisms that already have the information (genetic codes and protein machines) to make them. In a primordial soup, they would be very dilute or scarce, if present at all—certainly not sufficient for sustenance until an eco-system got going.

If we start out first with a one-celled organism, it would have had to be able to metabolize the molecules that existed then. As I pointed out early on, laboratory experiments have produced simple organic compounds from naturally occurring gases. However, the yield is very small, and the concentration of energy-giving substances is also very small. The likelihood of enough nutrients being available to sustain this one-celled creature is very low; most likely, it would not survive very long. If it had not invented cell division yet, it would be the end of the line.

Actually, the problem is far worse for the Miller experiment scenario, because Miller used the wrong gases! Researchers today do not believe that methane, ammonia or hydrogen were present in large quantities on the early earth. Instead, the atmosphere would have contained mostly carbon dioxide and nitrogen with some water vapor. When spark-discharge experiments are done with those gases, very, very few amino acids are produced. Another problem is oxygen. It is probable that some oxygen was present in the early earth atmosphere. The problem with oxygen is that it destroys the amino acids and other desirable compounds faster than they are produced! A third problem, rarely appreciated by those outside the field, is that amino acids come in two forms, left-handed and right-handed. Like your hands, they are mirror images of each other. For unknown reasons, life uses only left-handed amino acids for its proteins, and only right-handed sugars for DNA and RNA. Researchers concur that molecules made of mixed hands would be useless.

More than chance

Here's the problem: before life existed, there could not have been any natural selection. Why? Because natural selection depends on accurate replication. With natural selection out, what else could cause single-handedness? There is no natural law known that would cause a chain of one hand to assemble, because both forms have identical binding energies. This leaves chance—and only chance—to assemble proteins of all one hand. The probability of getting a 100% pure one-handed chain of reasonable length for a functional protein is vanishingly small. It would be like flipping coins and getting 100 heads in a row. There's no toleration for less than 100% pure, because one amino acid of the opposite hand would destroy the ability of the chain to function like a protein.

But even if you got all the amino acids to be of the same hand, a chain would be useless as a random sequence of amino acids. Proteins are highly specified in their sequences, because they have to fold into a 3-dimensional shape. Most random chains will not fold at all. Unfolded chains are destroyed by the cell, because they are not just useless, they gum up the works. That's what happens in Alzheimer's disease: globs of misfolded proteins accumulate in the brain, stifling the activity of the good brain cells. The protein chains in living cells are either so precisely sequenced that they fold into their proper shape, or are guided by molecular machines called chaperones that help them fold. All of this is wondrous beyond expression, but believe it or not, I'm still oversimplifying!

Figure 5-8. Membrane channel
A complex membrane transport protein, which controls what passes through the cell wall

Let us look in more detail at one way nutrients get into the cell to provide the fuel for metabolism. A cell membrane is far more complex than suggested by the already-complicated molecular structure of its lipid molecules described earlier. It is studded with thousands of little gates where molecules move in and out of the cell (Figure 5-8). As long ago as the year 2000, biochemists recognized the astonishing specificity of so-called membrane transport portals, or 'gates' in the cell membrane. After studying these portals with nuclear magnetic resonance imaging, one report said,

> Only small neutral molecules can pass unaided through cell membranes. Other kinds of particles—ions that mediate neural signaling, sugars that provide energy, amino acids that form proteins leave and enter cells through specialized molecular

portals known collectively as membrane transport proteins. To do their vital jobs, these proteins must recognize and grant passage, when required, to only one kind of molecule.[4]

Subsequent research has shown that these portals contain *specificity filters* that carefully discriminate between similar molecules. Some have moving parts like swinging doors or rotating leaves like the iris in a camera that control entry and exit. This is an ongoing field of research. One researcher won the Nobel Prize in 2003 for figuring out how just one gate works that pumps sodium into the cell.[5] It is essential for the functioning of nerves.

The structure of one portal figured out using nuclear magnetic resonance imaging is shown in Figure 5-8. In the figure, membrane channels in green appear within the gold-colored lipid molecules that make up the membrane. A specificity filter in the channel allows only desired proteins or molecules to enter the cell. Could random, undirected combinations of atoms and molecules in a 'primordial soup' have formed thousands of these portals on the first cell wall of the first cell? Simple holes in the membrane would not be able to discriminate between good and bad molecules. By the laws of osmosis, the bad would tend to leak in, and the good to leak out. Yet without any portals, the membrane would be a death trap. We can see that active transport had to work from the beginning.

Climbing the ladder of life

Consider the variety in microbial life. Even among one-celled organisms, there is a huge variety of species existing now. Each has characteristic shapes, structures and functions that differ from each other in sometimes dramatic ways. As we discussed earlier, diatoms build ornate glass houses of exquisite beauty and geometrical design—some shaped as squares, triangles and even five-pointed stars. There are over 100,000 species of diatoms, and we have not even begun to describe the

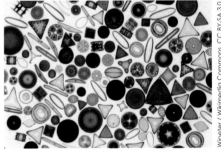

Figure 5-9. **Miniature ornaments**
Diatoms— algae that build microscopic glass houses

variety of one-celled organisms. If life started with some primitive cell somehow, all this differentiation had to take place over time. If all these descended from the first microbe, the number of successful mutations, even for single-celled life forms, would have had to be astronomical. (Think again; how many beneficial mutations did I see in the lab?)

Next as we climb the ladder of life, we could ask how or why animals differentiated from plants. Animals do not make their own food, but plants do. Did one evolve from the other? Which was first? That's a big question among origin-of-life researchers. They don't really know. Microbiologists divide the world of one-celled organisms into Archaea (presumably the oldest), Bacteria, and Eukarya (eukaryotes, cells with a nucleus, including all the multicellular organisms, both plant and animal). Was it the invention of photosynthesis that created the first plant cell? But some animals are capable of photosynthesis, too. It's a toss-up whether the supposed first eukaryote was plant or animal, the latter having the capability of movement, of taking in nutrients made by plants. But how did each get along without the other?

The ocean contains much animal life today, and this is the basis of the food chain. How did the differentiation between plant cells and animal cells take place? It must have required a mutation in a eukaryote that drove two cell types apart. The difference between plant and animal life is quite well understood and recognized. There are a few species that bear characteristics of both, but, particularly in the higher forms, the difference is profound. To imagine photosynthesis emerging spontaneously in the first plant cell is like imagining a solar power plant coming together all at once by chance.

It's common in the origin-of-life literature to hear scientists say that life 'emerged' somehow in the distant, unobservable past. But *emergence* of something as complex as a minimal cell surely would be synonymous with a miracle. That's not all that had to mysteriously appear by mysterious, unknown processes. Many of these same scientists claim that our Spacecraft Earth emerged, the passengers emerged, and the universe emerged. We'll consider that in the next chapter.

ENDNOTES

1.   Benton Clark, in Defining Life, *Astrobiology Magazine*, 19 June 2002, astrobio.net/

origin-and-evolution-of-life/defining-life.

2. *Origin: How Did Life on Earth Begin?* Illustra Media, 2016, originthefilm.com. See the "Clips" tab for excerpts.

3. Thomas, B., ATP synthase: majestic molecular machine made by a mastermind, *Creation* **31**(4):21–23, October 2009, creation.com/atp-synthase. An embedded video shows how the rotary engine works.

4. *Physics Today*, p. 19, September 2000.

5. Roderick MacKinnon shared the Nobel Prize in Chemistry 2003 for his elucidation of the structure of a potassium channel. See nobelprize.org/nobel_prizes/chemistry/laureates/2003/mackinnon-lecture.html.

6

The Final Frontier

How did the universe begin? Is it a surprising cosmological accident? That is the 'big picture' question, the biggest in all of natural science. The field of science that addresses this question is called *cosmology*. To be more precise, *cosmogony* deals with origins, and *cosmology* is the study of the nature of the universe. In normal usage, though, cosmology is more frequently heard in discussions of the big bang. It's interesting that the *cosmos-* part comes from a Greek word meaning ornament or design, while the *-logos* part refers to 'word' or information. Most cosmologists today, though, would never say a 'word' about 'design'. They are convinced that the universe made itself. It's their starting assumption: no information or intelligence from outside the universe should be included in any scientific explanation. But how can something make itself? The answer, they say, starts with a bang—a big one.

The big bang

Since the mid-1960s, the leading theory for the origin of the universe has been the 'big bang' theory. It edged out its main competitor about that time, the 'steady state' theory. The 'steady state' theory proposed that the universe is making itself all the time; new matter continuously pops into existence from nothing. The big bang, by contrast, made everything from nothing at the beginning. And so, the two leading theories for the origin of the universe in the 20th century have taught that everything comes from nothing—whether spread over time, or all at once. To many people, this seems like magic without a magician, but very few secular cosmologists doubt it. One leading cosmologist even wrote a book titled, *A Universe from Nothing*.[1]

The primary evidence cited for the big bang is (1) the alleged expansion of the universe, and (2) the cosmic background radiation. In the early 1900s, astronomers detected redshifts in the spectra of distant galaxies. The more distant the galaxy appeared to be, the more some well-known dark lines in the spectrum were shifted toward the red. Leading astronomers interpreted this redshift as an indicator of receding motion, analogous to how the sound of a car horn gets lower in pitch as it moves away. It suggested to them that all the galaxies are moving away from us and from one another: the farther away, the faster they must be moving apart. In this interpretation, the galaxies would have been closer together in the past. They surmised that if you could run a movie of the expansion in reverse, the galaxies would get closer and closer together. Would they converge at a point in the distant past? Big bang cosmologists think so; they interpret redshift as the expansion of the universe, and use it as strong evidence for the theory.

The other primary evidence used to support the big bang theory is the cosmic microwave background radiation, or CMB. Discovered in 1964 by two astronomers, Penzias and Wilson, this radiation is believed to bathe all of space. Theorists consider it to be the 'echo' of the big bang, gradually cooling from its initial hot flash, so that now, 13.78 billion years later in the big bang timeline, it has cooled down to microwave temperatures. The spectrum of the CMB fits the shape of the kind expected from a warm object. It is extremely uniform, varying less than one part in 100,000. In recent years, high-precision instruments have mapped out tiny fluctuations in the CMB. These fluctuations, cosmologists teach, were the 'seeds' of the galaxies we observe today.

That's a quick overview of the big bang theory and

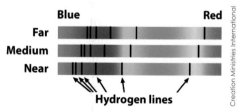

Figure 6-1. Redshift
Galaxies that are farther away have spectral lines shifted further toward the red end of the spectrum, allegedly indicating that they are receding faster than nearby galaxies.

Figure 6-2. Cosmic microwave background
Evidence for the big bang? Or a challenge to the conventional cosmology?

why most cosmologists believe it to be a true and accurate history of the universe.

In a simplified presentation, it has a certain intuitive feel, and like evolution, it is taught as fact and rarely questioned these days. I'm sure in your experience, though, that the closer you look at something, the more questions come up. Let's see if that holds true here.

Infinite density?

The big bang starts with everything in the whole universe compressed into an exceedingly dense form called a singularity. It requires that all of reality—all space, time, and mass-energy—began in this incredibly dense state, out of which all the stars, galaxies and planets evolved. Some say that the universe was in a state of infinite density and infinite temperature! And then somehow, 13.78 billion years ago, this singularity began to expand with the creation of space and time. As the expansion proceeded, matter condensed into clouds of particles that condensed further into galaxies, stars, and planets.

Let's think about what this means if reality started as one infinitely-dense hot blob. This is the way I would approach visualizing a condensed universe, trying to imagine everything as a singularity that somehow 'banged' at a particular point in time. I want to know, first of all, whether such a condition is even possible.

The total mass in the visible universe is, by some estimates, approximately 2 x 10^{49} tons. In ordinary notation, 10^{49} is a 1 followed by 49 zeros; in popular language, it's ten trillion trillion trillion trillion. (You recall that each additional zero multiplies the number by 10, so that 100 is ten times ten, 1,000 is ten times a hundred, and so on.) So the visible universe contains, roughly, 20 trillion trillion trillion trillion tons in mass. For comparison, the mass of the earth is approximately 6×10^{21} tons. The mass of the sun is 2×10^{27} tons (around a million times more massive than the earth). Think about how dense and compact the entire visible universe had to be if it started in one ultra-dense state! But cosmologists seriously believe that all of reality, including all the mass and energy in the entire universe, and all the physical forces, condensed out of a universe that rapidly expanded out of the initial universal singularity.

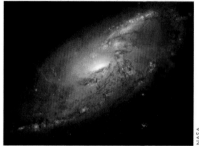

Over the past few decades, astronomers have discovered what they call black holes, which are bodies of such high density that their gravitational attraction prevents anything that falls into them from getting out. Not even light can escape. Some supermassive black holes, such as one believed to exist

Figure 6-3. **Galaxy NGC 4258**
The nucleus of this spiral galaxy contains a supermassive black hole.

at the center of Galaxy NGC 4258 (see Figure 6-3), contain tens of millions of times the mass of our sun. Physicists can barely wrap their heads around the possibility of all that mass, which continues to exert gravity, contracting into a singularity where the concepts of time and space break down. How much less can they understand the alleged universal singularity that became our universe! It would have been completely outside our experience, unapproachable by any methods of science. Even the familiar forces we learn about in physics allegedly developed from some indefinable state. It is difficult to comprehend how this 'whatever-it-was' could even have begun expanding. For these reasons, cosmologists cannot offer scientific descriptions of the singularity, but prefer to start their theory after it already existed: as close as 10^{-34} second after the expansion began, but after the beginning nonetheless.

Science is supposed to deal with observable phenomena. We can observe pulsars, quasars, magnetars and many other bizarre and exotic objects in the present, and try to make sense of them. I once read an astronomer's analysis of one X-ray source which consists of two closely orbiting stars locked in a fatal embrace. One is a tiny whirling neutron star (the exhausted, drastically collapsed core of a giant star), just a dozen miles across. Its life as a star is effectively over, its insides the equivalent of a cooling atomic reactor. This neutron star has more mass than the sun in a highly condensed state. So powerful is the gravity of the neutron star, its protons and electrons are thought to have been squeezed by gravity into neutrons. It is essentially a giant atomic nucleus! And yet it retains all the gravitational force of its massive progenitor's core (the part that remained after a supernova blew the outer layers out into space). On earth, one teaspoon of a neutron star would weigh about a billion tons. This corpse of a star exerts a powerful influence on its companion, hastening its demise by sucking its atmosphere right off. The neutrons do not collapse further because of a quantum property of atoms that is strong enough to resist further squeezing. In a black hole, however, no known force can overcome further gravitational collapse into a singularity.

For bizarre objects like these, theoretical physics gets pushed to the limit trying to explain them. But at least they are based on observations. With the big bang, though, there are no observations of a singularity expanding, and no analogues to anything with which we are familiar. What was it? Nobody knows. What came before it? Nobody knows. What caused it? Nobody knows. Secular cosmologists pride themselves on models that purport to explain what happened after the expansion began, even up to 10^{-34} second afterward. But it's notable that the observable objects we have been discussing (neutron stars, black holes and the like) are products of decay and destruction, not of processes undergoing creation and elaboration. The big bang violates two of the best-known laws in all of physics, the law of conservation of mass-energy (the First Law of Thermodynamics), and the law of entropy (the Second Law of Thermodynamics). It also violates a basic law of logic, that everything that begins to exist has a cause.

Admitted problems

For the sake of argument, let's assume there was a singularity that began to expand. It's a bit like the joke about two hungry men finding a can of tuna, wondering how to open it. One of them must have been a cosmologist; he said, "Assume a can opener." Even granting this very generous assumption that a hot, dense, uncaused, indescribable something began to expand, the problems are only beginning for the big bang theory. Cosmologists have long recognized four serious hurdles getting from a singularity to the highly structured universe we see today.

The Horizon Problem. In an expansion, there are parts heading one way that will never mix with parts going the opposite way. One would expect different regions of the universe, therefore, to differ substantially in temperature from each other. That's not what is observed. At the largest scales, the universe looks fairly uniform. Look north, and you see galaxies and clusters that are pretty much the way they look in the south. The temperature of the cosmic microwave background (CMB) is exceptionally uniform to one part in 100,000 all over the sky.

The Flatness Problem. Our universe appears poised on a knife edge between expansion and contraction. Space-time, according to cosmologists, could be curved one way, like a sphere, or curved the opposite way, like a hyperbola (picture a saddle shape extending out to infinity). Between those extremes is one and only one 'flat' shape (though we mean flat in three dimensions, not two). That's very close to what cosmologists think they measure. Recently astronomers have claimed to find evidence the expansion is accelerating, but it is still surprisingly close to flat. The probability of that resulting from an undirected 'bang' seems extremely remote.

The Lumpiness Problem. Except at the largest scales, the universe is 'lumpy'—it contains dense objects like stars separated by large distances of empty space. The stars are not randomly distributed, but are organized into galaxies. The galaxies are not randomly distributed, but are organized into clusters of galaxies separated by huge voids. One would expect an expanding soup of particles

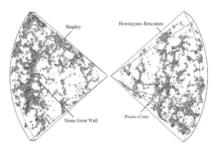

Figure 6-4. Lumpy universe
This map of large-scale structures in the universe shows alternating voids and giant superclusters of galaxies.

to end up with a more uniform appearance. All of this structure is supposed to come from the slightest variations in the CMB, but it is not obvious how to get from there to here, from an expanding fireball into the beautiful spiral galaxies that the Hubble Telescope has made a joy to behold. The lumpiness problem has been exacerbated in recent years by growing evidence that mature stars and galaxies exist at higher and higher redshifts. For the big bang, this would mean they had to form very rapidly after the big bang, not long after the first atoms condensed from the fog of expanding radiation. The problem is further worsened by continuing discoveries of large structures made up of galaxy superclusters called 'great walls' reaching across vast distances. There should not have been time for such structures to have formed.

The Entropy Problem. Everything in the universe proceeds from order to disorder, except where energy is channeled by either design or a force such as gravity (even then, the low-entropy state is only temporary, because stars explode or cool). A high-entropy, disordered state, therefore, would be expected for an un-designed, accidental universe. The big bang could have resulted in a uniform sea of particles, for instance. Or, everything could have wound up inside black holes. Obviously, that is not what we see. Mathematician Roger Penrose has called attention to this problem, pointing out that the low-entropy universe we see today would have had to begin at even lower entropy at the beginning—fantastically, incredibly low entropy, beyond our wildest imaginations—like one chance in 10 to the 10th to the 123rd power![2] There are not enough atoms in the universe to represent how many zeros that number would take to write out. It would be equivalent to a miracle.

Inflation a solution?

So serious were these problems, big bang cosmologists breathed a collective sigh of relief in 1980 when Alan Guth, a cosmologist at MIT, proposed a solution he called 'inflation'. In the first tiny fractions of a second after the expansion began, he proposed, the universe expanded exponentially faster than it does now, sending space-time and everything within it flying apart at fantastically rapid rates. In his mind, the universe suddenly inflated from the size of a beach ball to ten times the diameter of the visible universe (26 orders of magnitude) in one hundred billion trillion trillionth of a second![3]

(This didn't violate Einstein's cosmic 'speed limit' of the speed of light, cosmologists say, because the universe itself was expanding, not the matter inside the universe.) Guth compared inflation to the phase changes we all learned about in chemistry, when we observed liquid rapidly condensing or evaporating at a constant temperature. That was only an analogy; nobody knows if a comparable process could occur for an expanding fireball of space-time. But it solved the flatness problem and the horizon problem, he said, because any temperature differences or wrinkles in space-time would have been smoothed out in that tiny, infinitesimal fraction of a second. (We note that it did not solve the entropy problem or the rapid formation of galaxies.) Interestingly, Guth admitted in 2014 that he was motivated to pursue this 'answer' because the universe looked too perfectly designed—and too young—to have evolved.[4]

Shortly after this proposal gained popularity, others realized that there would be no way to stop inflation once it started. The theory has undergone several revisions since, such as 'chaotic inflation' proposed by Andrei Linde in 1983, which remains the most accepted version. Linde speculated that inflation continues to happen in parts of the universe we can't see! Needless to say, all such proposals border on fantasy. They look like cases of special pleading, using ad hoc 'theory rescue devices' to avoid facing the implications of the uniform, lumpy, low-entropy universe we observe.

Inflation also provides no explanation for what 'ignited' the big bang, or what came before it. In fact, no cosmologist has an answer for that. They basically avoid those questions by focusing on developments later than the first nano-nano-nanoseconds after it began, shelving the origin and ignition questions for 'future research'. One thing they admit, however, is that whatever ignited the big bang had to be very, very, very carefully 'tuned' for the universe to turn out right. The tiniest change in the initial conditions would have made the expanding fireball collapse back on itself, or fly apart too fast for galaxies and stars to form. In fact, inflation itself would have had to be more finely tuned than the universe it tries to explain! You can't explain an improbable happenstance by proposing an even more improbable happenstance. 'Assume a can opener' indeed!

For those who still think the inflationary big bang theory is solid science, listen to what one astrophysicist said as recently as 2016:

We still have no idea what the vast majority of the universe is made of. We struggle to understand how the big bang could suddenly arise from nothing or where the energy for 'inflation', a very short period of rapid growth in the early universe, came from. But despite these gaps in knowledge, it is actually human nature—our tendency to interpret data to fit our beliefs—that is the biggest threat to modern cosmology.[5]

The fine tuning challenge

I can't begin to describe how finely tuned our universe had to become to contain stars and life, if it made itself without design. Since the 1930s, certain physicists have been noticing peculiar things about our universe: fixed values like the charge on the electron, the strength of gravity, and the comparative masses of subatomic particles. They've noticed that slight changes to these values, which appear to be arbitrary (i.e., they could be otherwise), would make life impossible. Stronger gravity, for instance, would make stars implode, but weaker gravity would make them unstable. These finely-tuned values are sometimes lumped into what's called the 'Anthropic Principle'. In its simplest form, this principle states that human life exists only because these values are finely tuned. A variation says that if they weren't finely tuned, we wouldn't be here to worry about the problem! Amusing as that may be, the fact is: we *are* here, and the values are finely tuned. They beg for explanation.

The list of finely-tuned values in the laws of nature and requirements for life has grown to upwards of 20 independent factors. Some of them are so precise as to be absolutely astonishing. The *geometry* of the universe is so precariously balanced for stability, for instance, that one writer said it would be like balancing a pencil on its point and coming back 13.8 billion years later to find it still standing.[6] Another physicist said to imagine a tape measure stretched across the universe, then to consider one spot on the tape representing the strength

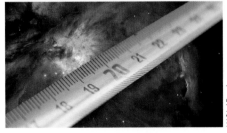

Figure 6-5. Finely tuned for life

Only a tiny range of physical values that could have governed the universe are life-permitting, which strongly points to design.

of gravity. Moving the value one inch either way, he says, would be catastrophic, making life impossible.[7] Any one of these factors seems impossible to account for by chance. Together, the improbabilities multiply into numbers that are beyond inconceivable. Is chance even an option?

Is the multiverse a way out?

To an unbiased observer, these factors appear to be designed for life. How can those who believe the universe created itself deal with them? Some of them have come up with a clever escape hatch: the notion that maybe ours is not the only universe. Maybe there are lots of universes out there—a 'multiverse' where all possible values for these physical constants exist. The reason we inhabit a good one is that we were lucky; we won the 'cosmic lottery'. You have to hand it to the die-hard materialist to be a creative storyteller. Realistically, this notion has major problems.

First of all, no other universe would be observable, even in principle, so the idea is clearly outside of science. Second, if there are an infinite number of universes, then anything could happen, and *will* happen, given enough opportunities: a thinking brain could pop into existence in space, or you could have an infinite number of clones in other universes doing any conceivable action. This would surely spell the death of scientific explanation.

There's a third and worse problem with it: it doesn't explain the origin of the multiverse. Where did the multiverse come from? We're back at square one, asking the very same question it was supposed to answer. We had better just come to grips with the universe we see.

Heat death and other dark matters

There is no one big bang theory; there are several versions, and they are always in a state of flux. So it's misleading to talk about 'the' big bang theory. The consensus view could be replaced tomorrow, and it might, because today's version is quite incredible. To make it work, big-bang cosmologists have had to dream up mystical phenomena called 'dark energy' and 'dark matter' that supposedly make up 96% of the mass-energy content of the universe. This implies that modern cosmologists, by their own admission, only have a grasp on 4% of what exists! Multi-year searches, using expensive detectors deep underground, have ruled out several candidate particles for dark matter. Nobody has any idea what these 'dark' things are. They sound like something out of the occult. At best, they are placeholders for ignorance. And yet they are necessary for the big bang theory.

Another problem not often mentioned is the antimatter problem. A big bang should have produced equal quantities of matter and antimatter, but antimatter stars and galaxies are not observed. The only explanation they've come up with is that the big bang might have produced a very, very slight excess of ordinary matter, perhaps one part in 10^{50}. It annihilated the antimatter, and the universe is made up of that tiny fraction of ordinary matter left over. There is no way to test this in the lab. It sounds contrived, but nothing better has been put forward. The most recent measures show matter and antimatter to be, at the limits of current precision, perfect mirror images of one another except for their opposite charges. There seems to be no difference that would allow one to predominate over the other.

Finally, big bang cosmology leads to a bleak view of the future. It implies that, over billions of years of expansion, the universe will get darker as galaxies blink out of our visible universe. With no new matter coming into existence, the universe would grow colder and dimmer, till all life and physical processes come to an end—a *heat death* of the universe. It's a pretty dismal view of our fate, but the end may come sooner than cosmologists thought. In the late 1990s, astronomers found evidence for thinking that the expansion of the universe is accelerating. Many of them believe that the acceleration will continue, turning the lights out on distant galaxies, until nothing but our own galaxy would be visible. Finally, they say, the fabric of space-time itself would rip apart.

That makes me think of another question. If darkness is fate of the universe, why hasn't it already happened? There's no reason to think we should be around right now to see hundreds of billions of brightly-shining galaxies all around us. Are we living in a special time that allows us to view so much of the universe and ponder its origin and meaning? Are we living in a special place?

Secular cosmologists don't like to think that there is anything special about us. They want everything to be explainable by ordinary laws of physics and chemistry, so that we are somehow a 'natural' outcome of those laws—nothing special. Yet here we ride on Spacecraft Earth, living on an ideal planet around an ideal star, kept alive by exquisite molecular machines, able to see galaxies billions of light-years away, with the ability to ponder the origin and fate of the universe. The number of cosmic coincidences that allow us to live, and breathe, and think is uncanny. Like pieces of a puzzle coming together to form a meaningful picture, our tour of Spacecraft Earth is leading us to think outside the box of commonly accepted explanations for origins.

ENDNOTES

1. Krauss, L.M., *A Universe from Nothing: Why There Is Something Rather than Nothing*, Atria Books, 2013. Note, despite the title of his book, Lawrence Krauss does not really believe in 'A Universe from Nothing' if that is taken to mean *absolutely* nothing. Nobody, upon reflection, can really believe that the universe came from absolutely nothing—no matter, no energy, no fields, no concepts, no categories. That violates the common-sense maxim, "Out of nothing, nothing comes." Krauss starts with a random fluctuation in a quantum field. But a critic could ask, 'Where did the quantum field come from?' Atheists often challenge theists, "If God made the universe, who made God?" The answer is that God, as a Person (not made of matter, not within the universe but transcendent apart from it) is eternal—the uncaused Cause that is both necessary and sufficient to explain our highly-ordered universe. An impersonal force or field cannot be an uncaused cause without leading to an infinite regress of questions like, "and where did *that* come from?" See also Batten, D., Who Created God? *Creation* **32**(4):18–20, October 2010, creation.com/who-created-god.

2. See video of Roger Penrose making this statement at evolutionnews.org/2010/04/roger_penrose_on_cosmic_finetu.

3. In his words, from "a patch as small as 10^{-26} m, one hundred billion times smaller than a proton, to macroscopic scales on the order of a meter, all within about 10^{-35} s." Guth and Kaiser, Inflationary Cosmology: Exploring the Universe from the Smallest to the Largest Scales, *Science* **307**(5711):884–890, doi: 10.1126/science.1107483, 11 February 2005, science.sciencemag.org/content/307/5711/884.

4. Vergano, D., Alan Guth: Waiting for the Big Bang, *National Geographic*, 30 June 2014, news.nationalgeographic.com/news/innovators/2014/06/140630-alan-guth-profile-inflation-cosmology-science. "In 1978, he learned in a talk by Princeton physicist Bob Dicke of a problem with the universe—it was too perfect. All sorts of factors, from the workings of atoms to the gravity holding stars together, seem too exquisitely fine-tuned for creating a cosmos in defiance of both rational explanation and what chance would predict," the article says. Later, Guth realized that if the big bang were true, the universe should be "swimming with cosmic defects. In fact, these defects should have been so numerous and so massive that if they actually existed, the age of the universe 'would turn out to be about 10,000 years,' Guth says, with a laugh." That's when he came up with inflation theory.

5. Kitching, T., Cosmology is in crisis—but not for the reason you may think, *The Conversation*, 8 January 2016, theconversation.com/cosmology-is-in-crisis-but-not-for-the-reason-you-may-think-52349.

6. Clark, S., The universe is flat as a pancake. Coincidence? *New Scientist*, 26 Oct 2010, newscientist.com/article/mg23230970-800-cosmic-coincidences-the-universe-is-flat-as-a-pancake.

7. Collins, R., in Strobel, L., *The Case for a Creator*, Zondervan, pp. 131–132, 2004.

ז

A Matter of Time

At this point, we've encountered a number of facts about the universe, the solar system, the earth, and those living forms that inhabit it. We've contemplated whether any kind of evolutionary mechanism could explain the intricate, sophisticated features we've studied along our journey.

All of the necessary features of the human physique and psyche are in place. All seem perfectly adequate to make the human body and mind complete. There is no obvious feature still in transition which, when completed, would provide an even better form. And I can say the same about essentially all of the life forms that we see around us. Each one is complete, matched to its environment, functioning as a member of its ecological niche. The fossil record shows a similar picture: a plethora of complex, functioning forms. As we've seen, the billions of transitional forms that should be there in an evolutionary scheme are, for the most part, notable for their absence.

We've encountered good reasons to question how much science understands these things. I speak as a scientist who has worked with scientists and taught science at the university level. What comes across in the popular press often does not reflect the amount of doubt, questioning and debate that goes on among the so-called experts. Even in my area of expertise among the 'hard sciences' of chemistry and physics, there is a great deal that is still puzzling. And sometimes, the experts get so locked into a mindset, they are unable or unwilling to 'think outside the box'. Are you willing to think outside the box with me, provided we let the scientific facts guide our thinking?

A number of years ago, I came across a monograph written by Dr Thomas G. Barnes, entitled "Origin and Destiny of the Earth's Magnetic Field".[1] Dr Barnes (1911-2001) was Professor of Physics at the University of Texas, El Paso, from 1938 to 1991. While he was still a professor at the university in 1973, he tossed a virtual bombshell into academia by showing, from a near century of actual measurements, that the earth could not sustain a magnetic field for billions of years.

Figure 7-1. Space pioneers
In this 1957 photo, Dr Henry Richter (left) and Dr George Ludwig (right) hold components that they designed for the Explorer III satellite, launched in 1958.

I have always been fascinated with the earth's magnetic field. One of the early things I wanted to do in terms of my earth satellite work was to map the geomagnetic field from orbit above the earth. Both Dr James Van Allen and I had this desire, beginning with his first experiment that we flew in Explorer I back in 1958. Had I stayed in the space program with NASA/JPL, this is the direction some of my work would have gone. When I came across Dr Barnes' book about the earth's magnetic field, I was quite intrigued about what he said particularly about the age of the earth. I will recap the gist of his monograph here, and then discuss the fallout of the debate that ensued.

Earth's magnetic field: "Tell us your secret"

The effects of earth's magnetic field were well known to the ancients, even long before magnetism was discovered or understood. They knew that a piece of magnetic lodestone or a magnetized piece of iron would tend to point in one direction; and so the earth's magnetic field was put to early practical use.

Inquisitive man attempted to explain the action of a compass, and in the early 1800s, discoveries were made which explored the relationships between electricity and magnetism. Means were devised to measure the strengths of these forces, and soon, fairly refined measurements were made which quantified the earth's magnetic field. Dr Thomas Barnes lists an early measurement made by Carl Friedrich Gauss in 1835. That started an ongoing list of measurements made from that time till 1965, which Barnes obtained from an ESSA government report (ESSA being the predecessor of NOAA, the National Oceanic and Atmospheric Administration).

Over that interval of 130 years, these measurements showed that the earth's magnetic field had decreased about 5%. Now, to me, that is a startling fact. I had always thought of the earth's magnetic field as being quite stable and unvarying. Since the 1830s, observations have shown that the north magnetic pole has wandered at about 55 km per year. More recently, geophysicists have uncovered indirect evidence that the field has reversed polarity—flipping over so that magnetic north aligned closer to the south polar axis, and back again numerous times. This inference is based on the fact that some volcanic rocks and minerals can capture the direction of a magnetic field when they solidify.

However, let me comment that science can only accurately examine what it can measure. No geophysicist has witnessed a reversal of the earth's magnetic field. The variations, moreover, are independent of the field strength. Think of a flashlight spinning slowly as its batteries wear down; it's that kind of thing. The magnetic energy is radiated out to space, where it cannot be used to regenerate the field. The orientation of the field in the past is inferred indirectly from rocks, since no one was present with a compass at the time. It's theoretically possible, of course, and we know that the sun's magnetic field

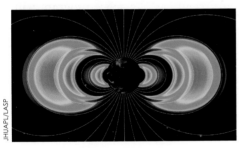

JHUAPL/LASP

Figure 7-2. **Declining magnetism**
The earth's magnetic field is losing energy.

reverses every 11 years. The magnetic fields of the gas giants (except for Saturn) all deviate from the polar axis. We should notice that the sun and the outer planets, however, are completely fluid, whereas the earth is solid and liquid. By contrast, the data on the strength of the earth's field, starting with Gauss in 1835, are direct scientific measurements. These are historical facts, produced by observation. To me, this is the best solid scientific data that exists concerning the earth's magnetic field. Theories should remain subservient to hard data.

Let me tell you, a decrease of 5% in the earth's magnetic field strength represents a huge energy change. The earth's magnetic field stores an immense amount of energy. To have this amount decrease by 5% in a little over 100 years represents an enormous loss of energy in a relatively short period of time. Calculations on this rate show that the field's half-life is 1400 years; in other words, in 1400 years the field strength will be half what it was. Some day in the future—should the earth remain and the decay continue—the magnetic field will effectively vanish.

Let me summarize Dr Barnes' conjecture as to what could have caused this decay. His book has a comprehensive mathematical treatment that explains the nature and change of the earth's magnetic field; I will spare you the technical details and give you a simplified explanation of what he had to say. It leads to a startling conclusion.

A decrease of 5% per 100 years, if considered back in time over the age of the earth, begins to add up very quickly. It's like the opposite of compound interest in a savings account whereby an account balance that pays 3% per year can accumulate a tidy sum in 50 years; it is this same kind of geometric progression. If we go backwards in time, increasing the magnetic field by 5% every 100 years, then we would know from simple arithmetic that 100 years ago the magnetic field was 5% stronger than it is today. 200 years ago it would be 10% stronger, and 300 years ago it would be 16% stronger, 400 years ago, it would be 22% stronger. Even though I am running time backward, this formula works exactly the same way as running time forward in an interest-bearing savings account. If we continue extrapolating back 1,000 years (ten 100-year periods), then the magnetic field would be about 1.6 times as strong as it is today. If we go back 2,000 years, it would be about 2.7 times stronger than it is today. Back 5,000 years, it would be almost 12 times what it is today. 10,000 years ago, the magnetic field would be 141 times as strong as it is today.

The magnetic field at the surface of the earth today is about 0.5 gauss (*gauss* being the standard unit of magnetic field strength). 10,000 years ago, the magnetic field would have been over 70 gauss—70 times as strong as the sun's surface! If we go back 12,000 years, the earth's magnetic field would have been about 190 gauss. If we go back to 20,000 BC, the strength would have been almost 10,000 gauss, which is stronger than the magnetic field in a sunspot, and could even be in some sense its undoing. So, if the theory of a 5% decrease every 100 years holds steady in the past, then as we get in the region of about 10,000 years, we would find that the earth had a very strong magnetic field, at 20,000 BC, an unbelievably strong magnetic field—so strong it would affect the habitability of the planet. One cannot extrapolate the field decay backward for millions of years.

Dating methods

Keeping that thought in mind, let me digress briefly and discuss one of the primary means of dating objects, particularly organic objects. The radiocarbon dating method was developed by Dr Willard Libby—one of my mentors—who won the Nobel Prize in 1960 for it. He reasoned that the age of an object could be determined if somehow we could measure the ratio between two isotopes of carbon, carbon-12 (^{12}C) and carbon-14 (^{14}C).

^{14}C is a radioactive element with a half-life of 5,730 years. As long as an organism is alive and exchanging carbon with the atmosphere by breathing and consuming plant food, then presumably the ratio of these two isotopes of carbon would match that which is present in the atmosphere at that particular point in time. When the organism died, it would stop exchanging carbon. At that moment, the ^{12}C to ^{14}C ratio would be locked in, and the radioactive clock would start ticking away. The amount of ^{14}C would steadily decrease

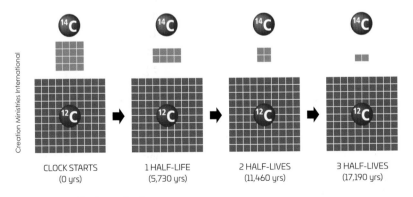

Creation Ministries International

| CLOCK STARTS (0 yrs) | 1 HALF-LIFE (5,730 yrs) | 2 HALF-LIVES (11,460 yrs) | 3 HALF-LIVES (17,190 yrs) |

Figure 7-3. **Carbon clock**
In a given sample, the ratio of ^{14}C to ^{12}C changes over time. The amount of ^{12}C remains constant, but ^{14}C is decreased by half as much every 5,730 years. Eventually, no ^{14}C will be left.

due to radioactive disintegrations. In 5,730 years (one half-life), the ^{14}C would decrease to one-half the original amount. In two half-lives (11,460 years), it would decrease to one-fourth the original amount, and so on. By measuring the ratio of ^{12}C to ^{14}C in a sample of dead plant or animal, based on the knowledge of the present ratio of ^{12}C to ^{14}C and the decay rate, we should be able to calculate how long ago the organism died.

I worked on the radiocarbon dating project at Caltech during my graduate days, and although it was fairly tricky to accurately measure the amount of beta particle radiation from the ^{14}C, we managed to do so quite well. However, the process is certainly not infallible. I distinctly remember one day when we decided to calibrate our system by measuring the apparent age of some recently dead plant material. We gathered some dead persimmon leaves from the backyard of my professor, Dr Donald Yost of Caltech. We burned the sample and extracted the carbon in the form of carbon dioxide. We then put our carbon dioxide into the counting chamber, and after we made the measurement and ran the calculation, we measured an apparent age of about minus 2,500 years! That meant that there was more ^{14}C than there should be, based on the present-day atmosphere. We soon realized that not far away at Yucca Flats in Nevada, some above-ground atomic tests had been performed after the war, and there was a small amount of radioactive fallout in the Los Angeles area. Some of this fallout must have contained ^{14}C, which ended up on the leaves that we burned, giving us an artificially high count of ^{14}C. So preparation of the sample is important.

However, let me go back to the effect of a large magnetic field thousands of years ago. ^{14}C is produced in the atmosphere when a nitrogen-14 atom is hit by an energetic particle, converting a proton into a neutron. This process goes on continuously in the atmosphere, producing ^{14}C at a steady rate as far as we know in modern times. Now, what would happen if a much larger magnetic field existed in the past? It would reduce the amount of radiation impinging on the atmosphere, and therefore would give us a much lower production of ^{14}C.

If we obtained a sample of the atmosphere 6,000 years ago and measured the ratio of ^{12}C to ^{14}C, we would find a much lower amount of ^{14}C than exists in the present atmosphere. We might be tempted to think, "My, this sample is very old, probably 20,000 to 40,000 years of age, based on the small amount of ^{14}C that is present." That's what the ratio of the two carbons would tell us. The lower amount would have been locked into any plant or animal material that died under those conditions. Using standard radiocarbon dating methods, we would be fooled into thinking objects were much older than they actually were.

We already know that corrections for atomic tests have to be made before calibrating the radiocarbon clock. What other corrections might be overlooked? That's an interesting train of thought to ponder. It means that we need to take radiocarbon 'ages' with a grain of salt. What scientists measure are isotope ratios, not actual ages. (This is true of all radiometric dating methods.) The calculated ages depend on assumptions; we can't always be sure we know all the factors that could have affected those ratios in the past. Nevertheless, for recent samples that can be calibrated against historical records, such as in archaeology, radiocarbon dating is useful and often reliable.

Source of the earth's magnetic field

Now, back to Dr Barnes' treatise: What causes the earth's magnetic field? There are only a few possible sources. One would be a large permanent magnet in the core of the earth. Another one could be a huge dynamo of some kind in the earth, which creates electric currents through the interior of the earth, and these currents create a magnetic field like an electromagnet does. Or, perhaps there are residual electric currents flowing through the inner portions of the earth which were produced at the origin of the earth, that are slowly decaying away. There are not many things that can produce a magnetic field, and these three explanations pretty much cover the gamut of possibilities. Let us examine these sources for the most plausible one.

First, perhaps the earth has a huge permanent magnet somewhere in its core. Now we know quite a bit about permanent magnets, and we know a fair amount about the interior of the earth. All permanent magnets that we can produce in the laboratory lose their magnetism when heated to more than a few hundred degrees centigrade; in fact, most lose their magnetism before that. It is quite unlikely that any kind of high temperature magnetic material exists that is unknown to science. We know that the interior of the earth is undoubtedly several thousand degrees, if not hotter, and so the likelihood of any kind of material maintaining a permanent magnetization at that temperature is not possible. So much for Explanation #1.

As for the dynamo theory, we know we can produce a magnetic field by running an electric current through a conductor. Except for the recently discovered phenomenon of superconductivity in a few materials at very low temperatures, electric currents decay and will not continue unless there is some driving source such as a battery, generator, or dynamo. Now, to say that there is some kind of generator in the interior of the earth that produces electric currents which produce a magnetic field leads to another question: What runs the dynamo? It takes power (energy acting over time) to operate a generator or dynamo. On the earth we use wind power, geothermal power, solar power or hydroelectric power to do it, but what continuous source of power over the eons could drive this theoretical dynamo? We know that perpetual motion is impossible. A dynamo cannot run without power to drive it, and so we can also quickly discard this second possibility.

This leaves the third explanation, that there are residual electric currents in the interior of the earth which are slowly decaying as they do anywhere in a laboratory or in our machinery. Let us surmise that perhaps these electric currents were created when the earth was formed. Electric currents die away because electrical resistance dissipates their power. On the other hand, currents tend to be maintained because of the phenomenon called inductance, which is an interaction between magnetism and electricity that tends to keep currents flowing if the current decreases.

We know that the rocks of the interior of the earth possess both resistance and inductance. If some simple calculations are made about the resistivity of the rocks of the earth's mantle and outer core, and also of the inductance characteristic of such matter, we can calculate the expected decrease of the current. Behold, Dr Barnes comes up with the figure that is approximately 5% every 100 years, nicely matching the historical decay measurements. So this third explanation has some apparent corroboration from theoretical studies. Explanations #1 and #2, however, are ruled out immediately.

Subsequent work by Dr D. Russell Humphreys in the late 1980s and 1990s extended and corroborated Barnes' work, but with modifications. Humphreys incorporated evidence from *archaeomagnetism* (inferences from archaeological artifacts) and *paleomagnetism* (inferences from volcanic rocks). Though not as robust as the real-time measurements made since 1835, these data, Humphrey feels, need explaining. The archaeomagnetic and paleomagnetic data, he says, contradict the assumptions of a steady decay rate. Instead, he posits a period in the third millennium BC when the field intensity fluctuated wildly, reversing polarity, dropping, and rising multiple times to former levels. The intensity reached a new peak about the time of Christ and has decayed steadily ever since. As a biblical creationist, he interpreted the fluctuations to be a result of flows in the mantle at the time of the Genesis Flood. Whether or not you, the reader, can accept that connection, the important fact that is undeniable is that the overall strength of the field (the amount of energy in the field) has declined steadily anyway, losing at least half its energy every 1,400 years.

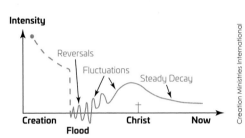

Figure 7-4.
Earth's magnetic field intensity
Dr Russell Humphreys believes the earth's magnetic field underwent several rapid reversals during Noah's Flood, but has declined overall since the beginning.

Creation Ministries International

A way to keep it old?

Surely secular geophysicists are aware of this problem. Some ignore it, thinking other evidence proves the earth to be much older. Some try to attack the credibility of Barnes and Humphreys. Most simply assume that someone else has figured out a solution that will keep the magnetic field going for billions of years. The favored explanation is that a permanent dynamo runs in the earth's interior (explanation #2). Somehow, this dynamo is sustained by convection, orbital mechanics, or residual heat from the core. (One critic of Barnes' theory says that "This dynamo is driven by an unknown energy source.") They've been working on this problem for over half a century with limited success. As we said, though, one cannot get something from nothing. Energy dissipates over time; the magnetic field energy is radiated to space, where it is no longer available to power the field. It should be decaying, and measurements show it is decaying. Even if reversals occurred during earth's existence, the overall strength could not have climbed higher than what it was before. It would have decayed at those times, and continues to decay now.

Consequences of magnetic field decay

What this inevitably leads to (and it certainly led me to), is the realization that our Spacecraft Earth is young. Instead of an earth that is 4.5 billion years old (an assumption never questioned by earth scientists and evolutionary biologists these days), it must be only thousands of years old. Why? If the earth were more than 12,000 to 15,000 years old, life could not exist. If we extrapolate backward in time the observed decay rate, huge magnetic fields would have existed at that time, and the earth would be physically unstable. Electric currents that powerful, flowing in the mantle to create these huge magnetic fields, would cause tremendous heating, to the point of melting the earth's crust. Heating over a shorter period of time is perhaps one reason why the earth's core is hot today.

If the dynamo theory were correct, Mercury should have no magnetic field, because (due to its smaller volume) it should have solidified long ago. Imagine the surprise when the spacecraft Mariner 10 in 1974 found a small but global magnetic field at Mercury about 1% the strength of earth's magnetic field. Those measurements were corroborated by the more recent MESSENGER orbiter, which also found that its magnetic field is decaying at a rate consistent with Humphreys' predictions.[2] This only makes sense if the dynamo theory is incorrect and Mercury is young, too. In addition, indirect evidence shows that our moon once possessed a magnetic field that has since vanished. Magnetic fields do not last forever.

The magnetosphere: our protective bubble

We should consider ourselves very fortunate to have a strong magnetic field. As the earth flies through space around the sun, we travel in a magnetic bubble called the 'magnetosphere'. This magnetosphere was essentially recognized and confirmed through the radiation measurements made by the Explorer I satellite, for which I had the design responsibility at NASA/JPL, and which flew the Van Allen cosmic ray experiment. The magnetosphere, which contains the Van Allen Radiation Belts, protects the earth from deadly radiation: high-energy charged particles streaming in the solar wind, and cosmic rays from outer space. The stronger the magnetic field, the more difficult it is for radiation to bombard a planet. One of the most common sources

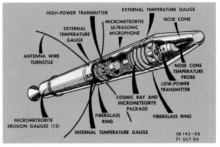

Figure 7-5. Explorer I satellite
The first spacecraft to detect the Van Allen Belts

of cancer and aging is particle bombardment from space that causes genetic mutations. The more energetic rays also create free radicals in living tissue, cause breaks in the DNA chain, and are generally disruptive. (I described mutations briefly in Chapter 5 in the section on fruit fly genetic experiments done in my Caltech genetics lab.)

Now, what would be the consequence of a larger magnetic field that would surround the earth with a much more robust bubble through which our Spacecraft now rides? If lesser amounts of radiation got down to the earth's surface, then the degeneration of life forms would happen much more slowly. We know that ionizing radiation is harmful to living tissue. The solar system is bombarded by a steady stream of cosmic rays and their secondary particles. Much of this radiation is warded off by the earth's magnetic field,

Figure 7-6. **Space shield**
The magnetosphere protects us from harmful radiation.

thereby protecting the body. As we mentioned earlier, NASA worries about astronauts traveling outside the magnetic field, because they are exposed to more radiation, putting them at risk of cancer, blindness and other serious health problems. A consequence of a larger magnetic field in the past is that the ionizing radiation reaching the earth's surface would have been significantly reduced. This would have been conducive to greater health and longevity and is consistent with early human lifetimes typically several hundred years or more, as recorded in the Bible.

Conspiracy

Think for a minute about how geology and physics have 'conspired' together in this case for our benefit. If we consider the exterior of our planetary spacecraft, we find some remarkable things. Recently, new aspects of the Van Allen Radiation Belts came to light after twin spacecraft were launched in 2012 to study them in more detail. What the new Van Allen Probes found is that there is a very thin layer between the inner and outer belts that high-energy electrons cannot penetrate. Exposure to these 'killer electrons' over time would be fatal to life on earth, and would pose a risk to astronauts who venture beyond it. This layer is formed because of the precise structure of earth's magnetic field, and its field strength, which is produced by electric currents deep in the earth. The researchers were so surprised at this discovery that they called it a Star-Trek-like 'space shield' that protects the earth. None of the other rocky planets has a significant magnetic field, and so they are exposed to the onslaught of high-energy particles from the sun and outer space. Just look at our own moon for comparison. NASA knows that astronauts in a future space colony would have to live underground or in some other protective structure, and could only wander about on the surface for brief periods. This is also true of Mars.

Other 'coincidences' of astronomy and physics may not be necessary for life, but they provide humans a great opportunity to make scientific discoveries. In chapter 1, I mentioned *The Privileged Planet* by Gonzalez and Richards. In addition to solar eclipses, which opened the door to discoveries about helium and relativity, they list a number of other factors, such as our solar system's position in the Milky Way and the type of star we orbit. These factors not only make earth habitable, they also make Spacecraft Earth the best place in the galaxy from which to make observations about the whole universe. More recently, Dr Michael Denton produced a video, *Privileged Species*,[3] which reveals even more 'coincidences' that make human life possible on our planet. It almost makes one suspect a plan and a purpose!

It's truly remarkable that there's only a brief window of time in which the earth's field is neither too strong nor too weak so that life can exist. That period happens to coincide with the few millennia for which we have written records of man's existence on the planet. Notice, also, that none of the other rocky planets has a field as strong and protective as Earth's: not Mercury, not Venus, and not Mars. Only the Earth, with sentient observers, has a magnetic 'bubble' just right to permit complex life.

How much time is needed?

Many scientists today scoff at the idea of a young earth. Don't the rock layers, fossils, and many other things show millions and billions of years of earth history? Discussions about these and related matters are beyond the scope of this book. They have been addressed in detail by creation geologists—accredited scientists with PhDs who take the Bible seriously. They describe how a global flood in the days of Noah could have produced all the stratification and fossils rapidly. In fact, they show how the Genesis Flood explains the strata better than current slow-and-gradual secular models. For instance, the bulk of Grand Canyon's layers are flat and undisturbed, lacking the gullies and erosion that would be expected had millions of years passed. In several locations, secular geologists tell us that 10 million, 100 million, or 1,000 million years passed between layers without a trace—the next layer sitting comfortably on top of the lower one as if nothing happened! Science is supposed to be about what you can observe. You cannot observe a 'missing billion years'. The flat layers, stacked like pancakes, imply that the layers were formed rapidly, one after another, and that the canyon itself was carved quickly. In some places, strata said to be millions of years old are folded without cracking, as if they were still soft when perturbed. The Flood accounts for these observations.

A smaller but recent catastrophe provides additional support for rapid geological change. When the Mt. St. Helens volcano erupted in 1980, hundreds of feet of stratified sediments were laid down in that one event. The eruption created a large lake behind an earthen dam. When the dam ruptured in 1982, a mudflow cut through the downstream sediments in a matter of hours. Strikingly, the canyon that formed resembles the Grand Canyon—layers, meanders, side canyons and all—on a 1/40th scale. That's but one example of a large geological effect accomplished in a very short time. A small stream now runs through the canyon. An onlooker might be fooled into thinking the stream carved the canyon over long ages, if he didn't hear about what really happened.

If the reader is sufficiently interested in further pursing some of these subjects, there is a wide variety of literature available, much of it by reputable scientists in peer-reviewed, scholarly works. To me, the decay of the earth's magnetic field is a subject with which I was familiar, that I found particularly convincing. It still strikes me as one of the most irrefutable arguments for a young earth. And if the earth is young, all of Darwin's speculations about evolution over millions of years are so misguided we can dismiss them entirely and open our minds to alternatives that fit a young earth designed for life.

Whether or not you are prepared to question what 'most scientists say' about the age of the earth, I hope you will stay with me for one more chapter, as I share my personal story of where the evidence

David Coppedge

Figure 7-7. The 'Little Grand Canyon', formed by Mount St Helens
This canyon, 1/40th the size of Grand Canyon, was carved catastrophically from a mudflow that resulted from an eruption of Mount St Helens on March 19, 1982.

led me. Think of me as a fellow passenger on Spacecraft Earth eager to share some good news with a friend.

ENDNOTES

1. ICR Technical Monograph 4, Institute for Creation Research, 1973. For a summary, see Barnes, T., Depletion of the Earth's Magnetic Field, icr.org/article/182.
2. Humphreys, D.R., Mercury's magnetic field is fading fast—latest spacecraft data confirm evidence for a young solar system, *J. Creation* **26**(2):4, 2012, creation.com/images/pdfs/tj/j26_2/j26_2_4-6.pdf.
3. Available at youtube.com/watch?v=VoI2ms5UHWg.

8

From One Passenger to Another

We are all traveling this spacecraft together. It's large enough to hold and feed billions of passengers, but each one of us only gets to ride for a limited time. We enter and exit on a schedule we don't get to choose. But during our ride, we can make choices. Having roamed this spacecraft now for over nine decades, I want to tell you about some of the choices I made, some bad and some good, which may assist you for the rest of your journey.

One of the things that I hope stands out loud and clear in these pages is that everything about this spacecraft shows purpose and plan. It extends outward to all of space, too. If we look outside, we see a vast universe obeying laws of nature, from the whirling galaxies down to the subatomic particles. If we look inside, we see a diverse biosphere of astonishing complexity, from the largest whale to the tiniest bacterium, all enjoying a planet that is suited for their sustenance. From the east to the west, from north to south, from inside to outside, the evidence is clear. Our universe is a showcase of intricate and exquisite design.

We have looked at a number of plants and animals that are well matched to their habitats, whether on land, in the oceans, or in the air. We have looked at our own 'spacesuits', our bodies, and found that we are provided with all the chemical and physical properties that allow us to flourish.

There are scientists who teach that man is a mere accident in an uncaring cosmos. I want to suggest the opposite: the universe is made for man, not man made by the universe. We've looked at a lot of data points to support that. One fact I mentioned is that the earth's surface contains all the trace elements and metals that physiologists know are essential to a healthy being. It is well-known that the body needs traces of magnesium, selenium, potassium, iron, phosphorus, and more: just read the label on your vitamin and mineral bottles to see the 'minimum daily requirements' for these elements. They exist in the quantities needed in our surroundings and in our food. Considering all of the molecular machines at work constantly in the human body that utilize these elements, is it likely that random geological processes delivered them to us, some from deep within the earth? I think not. So I asked the question, "Are these vital elements available to our body and its metabolic processes because they occur in nature, or do they occur in nature because they are essential to a healthy body?" I am firmly convinced that it is the latter. A Creator equipped Spacecraft Earth with these ingredients because the passengers need them. Many scientists, I thought, are looking at the world from the wrong direction. They think it created itself from the bottom up. To me, it looked more and more like it was designed from the top down.

The thought that science has reality backwards came on me gradually. The more I worked with molecules, organisms and spacecraft, the more I began looking at the world with an engineer's eye. I knew from hands-on experience how much purposeful activity and intelligence went into making a rocket or an instrument. How much more, I reasoned, would intelligent planning go into building a spacecraft like earth? The next logical step, I realized, was to ask: who is the Designer? What is his plan? There must be a purpose in all this design; what is it? How does that relate to my life?

My story

At this point, let me tell you a little about my personal and professional life and how I got into this search. I was a hard-driven American entrepreneur whose primary purpose was to be a success and to prove it! I had several different careers, each one with that same driving motivation. Questions about a Designer were often put on the back burner.

After a short term in the Navy at the end of World War II, I entered the California Institute of Technology in Pasadena, California, determined to become a scientist. I did all of my undergraduate and graduate academic work there and thought I was headed for a career teaching in some prestigious university. When it came time to graduate, although I explored some teaching possibilities, I went to a technical placement expert who convinced me I should begin my career at the Jet Propulsion Laboratory. I began there in 1955, at which time JPL was a guided missile research facility, owned by the U.S. Army and operated by Caltech. I began work as a supervisor in an exploratory research group in the Missile Guidance Section of the Laboratory.

Figure 8-1. **Jet Propulsion Laboratory**
As it appeared in 1950

About the time that I went to work at JPL, a massive international effort was beginning to cooperatively explore our home planet from a variety of scientific disciplines. A program named the International Geophysical Year (IGY) was in the works, scheduled to coincide with the upcoming solar maximum period of 1957-58.

In planning for the IGY—which was to involve all of the earth sciences, geophysics and atmospheric physics—there was strong interest in exploring the environment above the atmosphere. Up until then, it was customary to explore the upper atmosphere by means of sounding rockets which would go up several hundred kilometers in altitude, make a few quick measurements and fall back to the earth. It appeared technologically feasible at that time to fulfill a 'thought experiment' by Sir Isaac Newton in the 17th century: to launch an object which would not come back but would go into earth orbit. For the first time in history, thanks to advances in rocketry, earth satellite capability was now on the visible horizon.

Two countries announced that they would attempt to launch an earth satellite during the IGY—the United States and Russia. These ambitious announcements created what was the beginning of the so-called 'space race'.

At JPL we were very eager to become the nation's go-to agency for both satellite development and rocketry. As part of the U.S. Army, we submitted a proposal to take on those roles. Proposals were also submitted by the Navy and the U.S. Air Force, a typical procedure in the Federal Government environment.

To our dismay, the Navy received the award, and they put together a projected earth satellite called Vanguard. Since this was an international scientific effort, they decided to develop all new rocketry and not use any existing military hardware. At JPL we had planned on using existing rocketry with which we were quite familiar and in which we had a great deal of confidence.

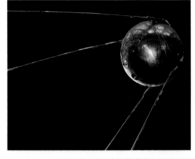

Figure 8-2. Sputnik
The Russian satellite launched October 1957

Then on October 4, 1957, the world was brought to full attention when it was announced that the Russians had launched an earth satellite called Sputnik. Our national prestige hit a significant low. On November 4, 1957, the Russians launched a second Sputnik, this time carrying a passenger: a dog named Laika. The Navy's program appeared to be in trouble as the scheduled launch for the first Vanguard test vehicle approached. The launch was a disaster. The rocket lifted only a few feet off the pad and burst into flames on live TV in front of the watching world. It was a national embarrassment, to say the least. America needed a success to catch up to the Russians.

President Eisenhower, impatient with the Navy's program, switched gears. On November 8, 1957, he directed the Army (specifically the Redstone Arsenal in Huntsville, Alabama, with Dr Werner von Braun in charge) to plan the next launch on the well-tested Jupiter-C rocket; and he directed JPL (with Dr William H. Pickering in charge) to prepare an earth satellite. The Jupiter-C used the liquid propellant Redstone missile as a first stage, and then three additional stages of small solid rocket motors made by JPL. JPL had developed these as scale models for its solid propellant tactical rocket named

Sergeant. In addition, JPL was directed to provide the earth satellite vehicle itself plus the radio tracking and communications equipment.

On January 31, 1958, the Jupiter-C rocket was launched at Cape Canaveral, with our satellite, named Explorer I, on top. Fortunately for us and for America, the mission was a great success. The free world's first earth satellite was in orbit. I must say, life changed dramatically for us in the program at that point.

The development of the satellite and its instruments was my responsibility. My team had been working for a couple of years on it even before we were authorized, 'just in case'. We also developed the communications 'microlock' link between the satellite and the ground. After the launch in Florida, I was part of the ham radio group that first heard the beeps from Explorer I as it passed over California, confirming that it had reached orbit. This led to a historic photo of Bill Pickering, James van Allen and Wernher von Braun triumphantly holding up a model of Explorer I over their heads at a hastily-convened late-night news conference, where scientists, reporters and the public were eager to hear the news. It made international headlines in the morning papers.

Figure 8-3. **Space triumph**
A model of Explorer I held by (left to right) JPL's Director William Pickering, scientist James Van Allen and rocket pioneer Wernher von Braun

Explorer I also made scientific history. After we had received an official go-ahead to build and launch a satellite, I recommended several scientific experiments for inclusion in the satellite, one being a small Geiger counter, developed by Dr James A. Van Allen (then at the State University of Iowa) to measure cosmic rays. In orbit, this little Geiger counter sent some puzzling data: there were periods when it went into saturation, exceeding the ability to count charged particles. Dr Van Allen interpreted this as showing that during certain portions of the orbit the satellite must have passed through a very high-energy radiation belt, previously unknown. Later found to be composed of several lobes, these radiation belts were named after him, and so are called the *Van Allen Radiation Belts* to this day. For someone like me just barely out of college and commencing his career, these were exciting times!

After a number of successful Explorer launches, the United States decided to develop a new agency called the National Aeronautics and Space Administration—NASA. Several organizations, including Redstone Arsenal and JPL, were transferred to become the nucleus of NASA. At JPL we were given the grandiose assignment of exploring the moon, the planets and deep space. That's a lot of real estate to be responsible for! I was appointed Chief of the Space Instruments Section at JPL, which had the role of developing and producing scientific instruments for the Ranger, Mariner and Surveyor spacecraft. From 1958 to 1960, I participated in those historic missions that led up to the Apollo moon landings. I also managed the planning and site selections for JPL's Deep Space Network, with its antenna complexes in Spain, Australia and California. These are still tracking spacecraft today.

Deeply involved in all this frenetic, history-making activity, I thought I was on the road to proving I could be a success. Unfortunately, life soon became tedious. Instead of being left to our own ingenuity, we were attached to a federal agency, with Congress and others looking directly over our shoulders. Frankly, this took all of the challenge and satisfaction out of the work. I soon felt I had no control over the areas for which I was responsible. I decided it was time to move on.

In 1960, I left JPL and joined a young high-technology research company in Pasadena named Electro-Optical Systems. EOS was involved in a wide variety of scientific, engineering and military projects. I felt that by getting into private industry there would now be a means of measuring my success: that is, whether or not the company prospered. I had become disillusioned in working for the government. I had come to the sad realization that in government work you get ahead by your connections, not your successes. I thought that by going into private industry, without the political interference, this disregard of success would be different.

I found at EOS that life wasn't different, because—it turned out—we had only one customer: the US Government! In our R&D role (research and development) at EOS, I did have a variety of fascinating scientific and engineering groups under my direction. But I did not feel I could take credit for the company's good performance, because in the start-stop world of government contracting, success is still no guarantee of getting ahead.

So I left EOS and went on staff at UCLA as a senior research geophysicist, working for Professor Willard Libby, the scientist who won a Nobel Prize for the carbon-14 dating method discussed in a previous chapter. I was assigned to be the Development Manager for a new proposed research campus. UCLA had been offered 450 prime acres in the Santa Monica Mountains to build a new interdisciplinary campus. My job was to put that project together, obtain the funding, and start the enterprise. Although I had an initial budget of half a million dollars from the University Regents' discretionary fund, Ronald Reagan became governor of California about that time, and—though many appreciated his fiscal restraint—it caused the state to tighten its purse strings significantly. My budget shrank to only 10% of its initial value. Now, one does not go to the funding agencies in Washington, D.C., looking for multimillion-dollar grants for a proposed new campus with only sketches of it on the back of a brown paper bag, which was all we could afford at that point! My hopes for success at that project were dashed, and it was time for me to move on again.

I bought a small company whose product line was standard time and frequency radio receivers. Now, I thought, I was going to prove myself in a business where the product was catalog price, with no government contracts. After several years I came to appreciate a lesson that Dr Abe Zarem, founder and president of EOS, had tried to teach us young managers, and that is there is only one thing worse than doing business with the government—and that is, NOT doing business with the government!

While I was at EOS, the company merged into the Xerox Corporation, and I ended up with a large number of stock option shares from Xerox, worth a considerable amount of money. In trying to make my small radio receiver business viable, I gradually cashed in all that Xerox stock till it was all gone. I suddenly had no resources left, and a business that was still losing money every month. Needless to say, this is a terrible predicament for an entrepreneur to be in. Worse than that, though, was the condition of my personal and family life. While pursuing my own selfish goals of success, I had let the most important things in life deteriorate to the breaking point.

It's with sadness that I tell you I was the proverbial workaholic and absentee husband and father. My family came apart, and I ended up alone trying to raise five kids, mainly teenagers still at home. Although my Caltech textbooks told me a great deal about this phenomenal physical universe and the laws that govern it, none of my academic training ever said anything about how to live life! I knew it was time to start learning that most important lesson. My goals for scientific success and business success left me disappointed. Meanwhile, because of my own pride and selfishness, I had proven very unsuccessful in my personal life and relationships.

The reason I am telling you all this is that in my desperate search for the meaning and purpose of life, I looked for some source of information to guide me, without realizing how close it was.

During most of my life I had gone to church, mainly because that was something respectable people did. I was active but not particularly devout. Our church had a 'textbook' called the Bible, but for a long time I never looked into it, feeling that ancient writings like that could not possibly apply to 20th century life.

A lady named Beverly, who had been my secretary at EOS, was with me at this low point in my life. She enjoyed a life of peaceful purpose that attracted me. We started spending time together and I found out she was a Christian. She talked to me about having a personal relationship with the Creator. So for the first time, I decided to really consider the claims of the Bible. I knew I needed help. I had heard preachers call the Bible the 'manufacturer's manual' for life. When all else goes wrong, they say, read the instructions!

I dug into the word of God and found, to my surprise, that the Bible speaks to people today, even in our modern scientific culture. It's not just an ancient book written by simple men but, rather, a library of 66 books written by 40 authors from all walks of life over a span of 1600 years. As I continued reading book after book—history, poetry, wisdom, practical advice on how to live, warnings, encouragements—I found it speaking to me as if alive and real. It had such incredible unity from beginning to end that I realized it had to have just one Author, and the only one who could begin to span that amount of time and geography had to be the everlasting Creator, God Himself. I began to absorb these fascinating sets of writings.

Then one day I was in my car driving on the 210 freeway to my little electronics plant in Monrovia, CA—another chance to look at the 'red ink' on my financial statement (more lost money)—and I suddenly felt the presence of Jesus Christ with me. All I could think of at that moment was: "Lord, if you want me, I sure want you". That was

October 4, 1969 (the twelfth anniversary of the launch of Sputnik, another day when my life had suddenly changed). I had agreed to a date with Beverly that night, and that was to go to Anaheim Stadium to hear a preacher I did not want to hear—Billy Graham. I did not tell her what had happened in the car, but I went with such joy and peace in my heart, it was unbelievable. When Dr Graham came to the point of inviting those in the audience that wanted to commit their lives to Jesus I was on my feet and heading down to the infield to make that call. Beverly was hanging on to me as she did not want to lose track of me in that huge crowd. After that experience, I felt washed totally clean inside—what a change!

His story

The name Jesus Christ was certainly known to me, but who was He? I had heard His name used in all sorts of manner over my years. However, who was He? C.S. Lewis said there are only four options: 1) a liar, 2) a legend, 3) a lunatic, or 4) legitimate. What does 'legitimate' mean? It means He was who He said He was, God come down to Earth for a very special purpose, and that purpose was to interact with His creation, me and the rest of you. So I picked option #4 and am so glad I did!

Now, looking back at all this, if you grant me that God exists, then doesn't it make sense that this God who created sentient beings like us would also desire to communicate with His creatures? He very definitely is interested! And how could God best communicate with us? It would be by entering that creation to allow direct face-to-face contact! Actually, that's exactly how it was in the beginning, before the first human pair chose to disobey Him, thereby breaking off that relationship. But because of his great love, He did not leave us without a means to reach out to Him.

God first gave us a blueprint for His creation, its purpose, and revelations about Himself in that book that we call the Bible. Beyond that, He came to the earth as one like us, fully man, but also fully God. When Jesus Christ was born a little over 2,000 years ago, His mission was to begin to re-establish that lost communication. It would not be easy. It would not be like swapping out a component in a communication channel. Disobedience had created a fundamental break that plagues the human creature, and that is our moral imperfection called *sin*. Jesus taught with great wisdom and authority, but His eye was to solving the sin problem.

You see, God desires a relationship with every person, but that relationship is not possible, trying to match one's corrupt earthly nature with that of a perfect Creator. There are those (and I was certainly among them) who thought that simply by trying to be good and do good deeds we can become acceptable to Him. But that doesn't work. All it takes is just one act of sin on my part, and I'm a sinner. We've all heard of the Ten Commandments; all it takes to sin is to break one Commandment either in thought, word, or deed. Don't our own courts realize that? If a thief tells the judge "I never murdered anybody," does the judge just let him off? How much more is a perfect, holy God, with complete knowledge of our thoughts as well as actions, going to hold us accountable? My sin makes me unfit to relate to God. Since we are already sinners, there is no way to develop a relationship with a perfect God from our side.

God realized this problem back before time began, and realized that a cure was needed for this sin problem. Being omniscient, He knew that man would choose disobedience. He therefore came to this earth in the body of Jesus Christ and paid the sin debt by shedding His blood, by hanging on a cruel cross to the death. Who could not stand in awe of love like that?

Wernher von Braun (the rocket scientist who developed the Jupiter-C that launched Explorer I) was a quasi-religious man for years, but became a devout Christian later in life. Like me, he was impressed by the exquisite design in nature, and believed in a Creator. But also like me, he felt the lack of a personal relationship with God. Despite his public persona and string of remarkable achievements, he came to a point, like me, when 'religiosity' and success did not satisfy his deepest

Figure 8-4. Wernher von Braun
In his office, September 1960

longing to know God and understand his purposes. After a friend shared the good news with him, and he accepted Christ, he became overwhelmed with gratitude for the love of God. Here's what he wrote shortly before he died in 1977:

> If there is a mind behind the immense complexities of the multitude of phenomena which man, through the tools of science, can now observe, then it is that of a Being tremendous in His power and wisdom. But we should not be dismayed by the relative insignificance of our own planet in the vast universe as modern science now sees it. In fact God deliberately reduced Himself to the stature of humanity in order to visit the earth in person, because the cumulative effect over the centuries of millions of individuals choosing to please themselves rather than God had infected the whole planet. When God became a man Himself, the experience proved to be nothing short of pure agony. In man's time-honored fashion, they would unleash the whole arsenal of weapons against Him: misrepresentation, slander, and accusation of treason. The stage was set for a situation without parallel in the history of the earth. God would visit His creatures and they would nail Him to the cross![1]

Incredible as that act of rebellion was, it was all part of God's plan. In fact, many prophets in the Old Testament predicted this treatment of Messiah, hundreds of years before the events took place (read Isaiah 53 as an example, written 700 years before Christ). On that cross, the work of redemption was done. "It is finished!" Jesus cried on the cross as he breathed his last. Then, after three days in the grave, he rose from the dead, telling his disciples to proclaim the good news to everyone throughout the world, that repentance and forgiveness of sins is freely available through His name. He paid the price. Now it's our turn to respond.

This payment for the sin debt is a free gift. There is no way that I can earn it by anything that I can do or give. What can I offer to God who created and owns the universe, to begin with? The only thing I can offer Him is myself—the only thing that God created in me that I have a choice about is my free will to believe Him. I can choose to believe all the evidence that He is the Son of God who died and rose again. I can choose to believe the promises of God that He forgives those who trust in His Son. I can choose to accept His free gift. By accepting this free gift, then I become a child of God for all of eternity and immediately become a citizen of Heaven. I discovered all this because Beverly cared enough to share her faith with me. Incidentally, I married her—47 years ago!

I didn't find that relationship in my life until I was past the age of 40, but I am ever so thankful that I did, because now I have a personal bond with the Creator of the universe! All those amazing designs I saw in nature now make sense. I have a purpose in life. I'm heaven bound. If you

Figure 8-5.
Henry and Beverly Richter

have not made this same wonderful discovery, I urge you to investigate Jesus for yourself. And find a church that teaches the whole Bible and honors Jesus Christ.

It's been a great joy to share with you the good news. "Believe in the Lord Jesus, and you will be saved" (Acts 16:31).

Now pick up a Bible and read the original, authentic *Passenger's Guide to Spacecraft Earth*!

ENDNOTES

1. Hill, H., *From Goo to You by Way of the Zoo*, Logos International, Plainfield, NJ, 1976.

Epilogue

There is a hazard in covering the subject of this book in a frank manner. The forces of political correctness and the intolerance of the scientific community can have consequences for those who espouse the biblical creationist point of view.

A case in point is what happened to my friend and collaborator, David Coppedge, who in his quiet but open way made his beliefs known at work at the Jet Propulsion Laboratory. It cost him his job, even though he had 12 years of good reviews and had been a Team Lead for nine years.

His trouble started one day in 2009, when he offered (in a low key way) a DVD about intelligent design to a co-worker. She complained to the boss, telling him the material made her feel 'uncomfortable'. The boss ordered David not to discuss 'religion or politics' with anyone, and reported him to Human Resources. He was investigated, demoted, and given a written warning not to 'harass' people with his 'personal views'.

When I found out about this, I wrote a letter on his behalf and delivered it to the Deputy Director of JPL. We knew each other because I circulated in top JPL circles during all the ceremony associated with the 50th anniversary of Explorer I the prior year. I also gave him a copy of a DVD featuring Ben Stein, *Expelled: No Intelligence Allowed*, that documented the discrimination scientists and journalists suffered for advocating intelligent design. The Deputy Director accepted it, and seemed familiar with and agreeable to Ben Stein. However, my letter had no effect and was simply forwarded to Human Resources to be added to the file against David.

I had already made my creationist stand known to top management at JPL, having sent half a dozen of them a copy of the predecessor to this book, *The Universe: A Surprising Cosmological Accident.* I got no comments whatsoever about the book or its content.

David obtained volunteer legal assistance from Christian attorneys, and filed a lawsuit for discrimination after exhausting internal remedies. JPL retaliated by firing him. It was a 'David and Goliath' contest between David's lone attorney and a battery of lawyers amassed by JPL and Caltech. I was not a party to any of the court proceedings, but after a five-week trial with 22 witnesses, a lone judge ruled against David with no explanation. Most had thought this would be a straightforward 'freedom of speech' matter.

So the hazard of bucking the scientific community is real; many must feel really threatened by the thought that there is a Creator and that we are accountable to Him. What a pity, and what a sad way to live, with no hope of eternal life! Fortunately, God has been good to David after this crisis, providing opportunities for him to become a science researcher and journalist. I am pleased he was available to assist me with this book.[1]

ENDNOTES

1. See Wieland, C., The Creation Safari Man, *Creation* 37(3):18–20, July 2015, creation.com/safari-man. David's account of the case can be found at davidcoppedge.com/jpl-trial-blog.html. The Discovery Institute posted numerous articles on the case, the latest by Klinghoffer, D., NASA Versus David Coppedge: Most Reprehensible Case of Anti-Intelligent Design Persecution Yet? 19 Dec 2016, evolutionnews.org/2016/12/david_coppedge103376.html.

ABOUT THE AUTHORS

Dr Henry Richter (left), after a short tour in the Navy at the end of World War II, earned a PhD in chemistry, physics, and electrical engineering from the California Institute of Technology. Dr Richter worked for NASA's Jet Propulsion Laboratory (JPL) during the space race, and oversaw the development of America's first earth satellite, Explorer I. He was also responsible for scientific instruments in the Ranger, Mariner, and Surveyor spacecraft. After several other careers, he is now retired and lives in Escondido, California, USA.

David F. Coppedge (right) worked at NASA-JPL for 14 years (1996–2011) as an IT specialist for the Cassini Mission to Saturn, nine years as Team Lead System Administrator.

RECOMENDED RESOURCES

The Creation Answers Book
Dr Don Batten, Dr David Catchpoole,
Dr Jonathan Sarfati and Dr Carl Wieland

Provides biblical answers to over 60 of the most-asked questions on creation/evolution and the Bible! Not only does it give satisfying answers—it will equip you to effectively engage those that resist the Gospel due to worldly teaching on origins. A 'must have' every believer's library!

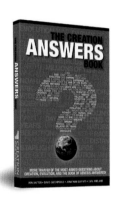

6 Days: Not Billions of Years!
Classic creation articles in a magazine format, covering topics that everyone wants to know about. What should we believe about ghosts and aliens? Why would a loving God allow death and suffering? How did Noah fit the animals on the ark? What about radiometric dating? Ideal for families, churches, and youth groups.

Evolution's Achilles' Heels
Dr Robert Carter (editor)

This powerful book (illustrated in full colour) exposes the fatal flaws of evolutionary thinking. Like no other work, it is authored by nine Ph.D. scientists to produce a coordinated, coherent, powerful argument. Each is a specialist in the field of the subjects addressed, including: Natural selection, the origin of life, geology, genetics, radiometric dating, the fossil record, cosmology, and ethics.

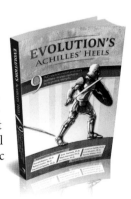

For more information visit
CREATION.com

CREATION.com

For more information on creation/evolution and Bible-science issues

---

AUSTRALIA
Creation Ministries International (Australia)
PO Box 4545
Eight Mile Plains, QLD 4113

Phone: (07) 3340 9888
Fax: (07) 3340 9889

CANADA
Creation Ministries International (Canada)
300 Mill St, Unit 7
Kitchener, ON N2M 5G8

Phone: (519) 746–7616
Orders & donations: 1-888-251-5360
Fax: (519) 746–7617

NEW ZEALAND
Creation Ministries International (NZ)
PO Box 39005
Howick, Auckland 2145

Phone/Fax: (09) 537 4818

SINGAPORE
Creation Ministries International (Singapore)
Clementi Central Post Office
PO Box 195
Singapore 911207

SOUTH AFRICA
Creation Ministries International (SA)
PO Box 3349
Durbanville 7551

Phone: (021) 979 0107
Fax: (086) 519 0555

UK & Europe
*Creation Ministries International
(UK/Europe)*
15 Station St,
Whetstone, Leicestershire, LE8 6JS

Phone: 0116-2848-999

USA
Creation Ministries International (USA)
PO Box 350,
Powder Springs, GA 30127

Phone: (800) 616-1264
Fax: (770) 439-9784

OTHER COUNTRIES
Creation Ministries International
PO Box 4545
Eight Mile Plains,
QLD 4113, Australia

Phone: +617 3340 9888
Fax: +617 3340 9889